OXFORD REVISION GUIDES

GCSE

CHEMISTRY
through diagrams

Michael Lewis

Oxford University Press

Oxford University Press,
Great Clarendon Street, Oxford OX2 6DP

Oxford New York
Athens Auckland Bangkok Bogota Bombay
Buenos Aires Calcutta Cape Town Dar es Salaam Delhi
Florence Hong Kong Istanbul Karachi
Kuala Lumpur Madras Madrid Melbourne
Mexico City Nairobi Paris Singapore
Taipei Tokyo Toronto Warsaw
and associated companies in
Berlin Ibadan

Oxford is a trade mark of Oxford University Press

First published 1997

New edition 1998 ISBN 0 19 914715 9 (Student's edition)
                      0 19 914716 7 (Bookshop edition)

Typesetting, design and illustration by Hardlines, Charlbury, Oxford
Printed in Great Britain

CONTENTS

Syllabuses for GCSE Science: Chemistry

The subject of Chemistry may be studied in the following ways at GCSE:

- with Physics and Biology as part of **GCSE Science: Single Award** (equivalent to one GCSE)

- with Physics and Biology as part of **GCSE Science: Double Award** (equivalent to two GCSEs)

- on its own to give **GCSE Science: Chemistry** (one GCSE). If you are also studying Physics and Biology as separate subjects, this may lead to a triple award in the sciences.

The following information relates to syllabuses for GCSE Science: Chemistry.

Core and extension - two areas of Chemistry

GCSE Science: Chemistry covers some subject matter which is called the **common core**, and also extra areas of chemistry called **extension material**. The common core is what makes up the chemistry component of GCSE Science: Double Award.

Foundation and higher - two levels of examination

The scale of grades at GCSE is A*, A, B, C, D, E, F, and G. It would be impossible to grade pupils from A* to G based on the same examination, as pupils expecting an A would find all the questions too easy, or pupils expecting an F would find them too hard. To overcome this problem, there are two **tiers** or levels of exam called **Foundation** and **Higher**. Pupils entered for the Foundation tier can achieve grades G to C, and those entered for the Higher tier can achieve grades A* to D.

Examining groups and syllabuses - which one are you studying?

There are several examining groups or boards that set syllabuses and examinations, which are listed below with their abbreviations. Make sure you know which group and syllabus you are studying for. You can obtain a copy of the syllabus and also sample examination papers from your examining group, which will give you a good idea of what to expect when your examination comes. Full details of how to contact the examining groups are given on page viii.

EDEXCEL: London Examinations
MEG: Midland Examining Group
NEAB: Northern Examinations and Assessment Board
NICCEA: Northern Ireland Council for the Curriculum, Examinations and Assessment
SEG: Southern Examining Group
WJEC: Welsh Joint Education Committee
IGCSE: International General Certificate of Secondary Education, administered by University of Cambridge Local Examinations Syndicate

As well as the ordinary GCSE in Chemistry, MEG also offers two alternatives: Nuffield and Salters'. The Nuffield approach is based on learning through practical investigations, while the Salters' approach starts with everyday situations to introduce scientific ideas in a realistic context. Nuffield candidates sit the same examinations as the ordinary Chemistry candidates, while Salters' candidates sit a different examination.

Assessment - how they award your grade

Your GCSE grade is based on two kinds of assessment: written **examinations** and **coursework**. There is one set of examinations for the Foundation tier and another set for the Higher tier, so you will sit either one set or the other. The examinations aim to test:

- your **knowledge** and **understanding** of chemistry - whether you can recall and use the subjects you have studied, and apply your knowledge to new situations

- whether you can **communicate** chemical information to other people

- whether you can **evaluate**, or take in and make judgements on, information that is presented to you.

Experimental and investigative work is assessed by coursework for both the Foundation and Higher tiers. Coursework is explained in more detail on page vii.

In general, the examinations account for 75% of the final grade and the coursework for 25%. Some examining groups set two examinations, usually with the first one covering just the core material and the second also including extension material. Other examining groups set just one examination. The details of the assessment structure for each examining group and syllabus are given in the facing table. Find your own syllabus on the table and make sure you know what you are expecting. The 'Weighting' column shows what percentage of the total marks is given for each paper or for the coursework. There is more information about the sort of questions that may may be set in examinations on page vi.

Assessment structure

Examination group/syllabus	Tiering	Papers	Length of paper	Weighting	Question style (questions compulsory?)
MEG					
Chemistry Syllabus A (1781)	Foundation G-C	Paper 1 (Core)	$1\frac{1}{2}$ hours	50%	Structured (all compulsory)
		Paper 3 (Extension)	$\frac{3}{4}$ hour	25%	Structured (all compulsory)
		Coursework		25%	
	Higher D-A*	Paper 2 (Core)	$1\frac{1}{4}$ hours	50%	Structured (all compulsory)
		Paper 4 (Extension)	1 hour	25%	Structured (all compulsory)
		Coursework		25%	
Chemistry Syllabus D (Nuffield) (1786)	Foundation G-C	Paper 1 (Core)*	$1\frac{1}{2}$ hours	50%	Structured (all compulsory)
		Paper 3 (Extension)	$\frac{3}{4}$ hour	25%	Structured (all compulsory)
		Coursework		25%	
*same as Syllabus A	Higher D-A*	Paper 2 (Core)*	$1\frac{3}{4}$ hours	50%	Structured (all compulsory)
		Paper 4 (Extension)	1 hour	25%	Structured (all compulsory)
		Coursework		25%	
Chemistry Syllabus C (Salters') (1791)	Foundation G-C	Foundation Paper	2 hours	75%	Structured (all compulsory)
		Coursework		25%	
	Higher D-A*	Higher Paper	$2\frac{1}{4}$ hours	75%	Structured (all compulsory)
		Coursework		25%	
NEAB					
Chemistry (1171)	Foundation G-C	Paper F	2 hours	75%	Structured (all compulsory)
		Coursework		25%	
	Higher D-A*	Paper H	$2\frac{1}{4}$ hours	75%	Structured (all compulsory)
		Coursework		25%	
EDEXCEL					
Chemistry (1036)	Foundation G-C	Paper 1F (01) (Core)	$1\frac{1}{2}$ hours	50%	Structured (all compulsory)
		Paper 2F (02) (Extension)	1 hour	25%	Structured (all compulsory)
		Coursework		25%	
	Higher D-A*	Paper 3H (03) (Core)	$1\frac{1}{2}$ hours	50%	Structured (all compulsory)
		Paper 4H (04) (Extension)	1 hour	25%	Structured (all compulsory)
		Coursework		25%	
SEG					
Chemistry (2660)	Foundation G-C	Core paper (2)	$1\frac{1}{2}$ hours	50%	Structured and free response
		Additional paper (3)	1 hour	25%	Structured and free response
		Coursework		25%	
	Higher D-A*	Core paper (4)	$1\frac{1}{2}$ hours	50%	Structured and free response
		Additional paper (5)	1 hour	25%	Structured and free response
		Coursework		25%	
NICCEA					
Chemistry	Foundation G-C	Paper 1	1 hour	30%	Structured (all compulsory)
		Paper 2	$1\frac{1}{2}$ hours	45%	Structured (all compulsory)
		Coursework		25%	
	Higher (E)D-A*	Paper 1	$1\frac{1}{2}$ hours	32%	Structured (all compulsory)
		Paper 2	2 hours	43%	Structured (all compulsory)
		Coursework		25%	
WJEC					
Chemistry	Foundation G-C	Foundation paper	2 hours	75%	Short answer and free response
		Coursework		25%	
	Higher D-A*	Higher paper	$2\frac{1}{2}$ hours	75%	Short answer and free response
		Coursework		25%	
IGCSE					
Chemistry	Core G-C	Paper 1	$\frac{3}{4}$ hour	40%	Multiple choice (all compulsory)
		Paper 2	1 hour	40%	Short answer and structured (all compulsory)
		Coursework			
		Paper 4 coursework or		20%	
		Paper 5 Practical test or	$1\frac{1}{4}$ hours	20%	Questions covering experimental and observation skills
		Paper 6 Alternative to practical	1 hour	20%	Written questions about laboratory procedures
	Extended A to G	Core Papers 1 and 2 plus Paper 3	$1\frac{1}{4}$ hours	80%	Structured and free response (all compulsory)
		Coursework			
		Paper 4 coursework or		20%	
		Paper 5 Practical test or	$1\frac{1}{4}$ hours	20%	Questions covering experimental and observation skills
		Paper 6 Alternative to practical	1 hour	20%	Written questions about laboratory procedures

Question types

Your examination may contain several of the same type of question, or it may contain different styles of question. The table on the previous page shows the question style set by each examining group. The main types of question you may come across are described below. Some sample examination style questions are given on page x.

Short-answer questions

These questions can usually be answered in one sentence, or with a drawing or equation. The answer is written in a space left on the examination paper, and the number of marks is given.

Structured questions

These are longer questions made up of connected parts. They are presented in the same way as short-answer questions, the main difference being that they enlarge on a topic in more detail. The number of marks is given on the paper for each part of the question.

Answering short-answer and structured questions

The space left on the paper gives you an idea of how much to write, and you should keep your answer brief and concise. Make sure you read the question carefully and don't give information that is not required. For example, if you are asked to *list* then do just that - don't describe or explain or discuss, you will waste time and you won't gain any more marks. The number of marks also gives a good indication of how much the examiner is looking for. If there are three marks for a 'list' question, then there will probably be three things to list.

If you are asked to sketch a diagram, then don't waste time making it look beautiful. It should be neat, clear and accurately labelled but not elaborate.

If you are asked to give an equation, read carefully to see whether it is a word equation or a symbol equation. Make sure all symbol equations are balanced and include the state symbols (s), (l), (aq) or (g).

In calculations, make sure you show all your working. Then if you make a slip at the end, you will still get some marks. A single wrong answer will gain you no marks. Don't forget to include units.

Free response questions

These are open-ended questions which require you to build up an explanation or argument in an essay-type answer. Free response questions are only set by a few of the examining groups. One question like this can carry quite a lot of marks.

Answering free response questions

You need to judge how much information to include, and how much you should write. It's a good idea to plan your answer to this type of question first, by making notes or sketches to organise your thoughts.

Make sure you read the question very carefully, because if you go off in the wrong direction you will lose a lot of marks. Use the number of marks to decide how much time you should spend on the question. If the question is worth 8 marks out of a total of 24, then don't spend more than about a third of the total time on it.

Try to be as neat and as logical as you can. This will help the examiner to find his or her way around your answers, and to award the marks quickly. Don't forget that spelling, punctuation, and grammar are important, and you will lose marks if your written English is sloppy.

Multiple choice questions (GCSE only)

In these questions, several alternative answers are suggested and you have to choose which one is correct. The examination paper requires you to fill in your answer in a specific way, and you will lose marks if you don't record your answer correctly. You may lose marks for an incorrect answer, so if you are really not sure it might be best to leave that question blank. The best preparation for this kind of question is to look at sample/past papers from your examining group and read the instructions carefully.

Don't write too much! Just answer the questions asked.

Coursework

Practical work, including investigations, will be marked by your teacher throughout the course and will count 25% towards your final grade (If you are taking the IGCSE exam then the arrangements are different - check with your teacher.)

There are four separate skill areas in which you will be awarded a mark:

- planning experimental procedures (P)
- obtaining evidence (O)
- analysing the evidence and drawing conclusions (A)
- evaluating the evidence (E).

These four areas are explained in more detail below. In most syllabuses you will be awarded a mark out of 8 or out of 6 in each area, with a small additional mark for spelling, punctuation, and grammar. Your teacher will tell you when you are going to be tested, and on which area or areas. You will have opportunities throughout the course to practise and improve your skills. Your best mark in each of the four areas will normally be used, though the marks must come from at least two different pieces of coursework, and one of them should come from a complete **investigation**. This means that instead of just carrying out an experiment according to instructions given to you, you are given a problem to solve. You have to decide what you are going to look at, what measurements you will take, how to measure them, how to present your results, and finally assess whether you have actually solved the problem or not.

Planning experimental procedures (P)

First read the problem carefully and think about what you are trying to find out. Then write a short plan including:

- the problem you are trying to solve
- the variables you will keep constant and the variable you will change. For example, if you are testing whether the speed of a reaction changes with temperature, then you will want to vary the temperature while keeping other variables constant, such as amounts and concentrations of reagents, and particle size.
- the apparatus you will need, perhaps with a labelled diagram of the set-up, and any safety measures you will need to take
- what you will measure, and how many readings you need to take
- your predicted results, such as: 'If I change this variable, then I predict that that will happen, because...'.

Obtaining evidence (O)

Here you are tested on your ability to carry out practical work. Follow your plan, or other instructions given to you, step by step and use apparatus carefully to make accurate measurements. Observe what is happening very carefully. If your planned experiment does not work for some reason, you can make changes to your method.

Record all your results carefully and clearly, either in a list or in a table with precise headings. Remember to include units. Repeat the experiment if you can, to obtain a second set of results. Repeat any readings you think might be inaccurate.

Analysing the evidence and drawing conclusions (A)

You need to present your list or table of results in a form that shows clearly what the experiment demonstrated. A graph is often (but not always) the best way of doing this. Put the variable that you changed along the x-axis, and the variable that you measured up the y-axis. For example, if you measured the total volume of carbon dioxide given off by a reaction every 30 seconds, then time (which you determined by choosing to take readings every 30 seconds) goes along the x-axis, and the volume of carbon dioxide (which you measured) goes up the y-axis. Label the axes and don't forget units. If you have results that don't seem to fit, you should still include them. You may be able to think of a reason why they are inaccurate.

Then draw conclusions. This means describing what your results actually show, not what you expected them to show! Comment on the shape of your graph and what this means. Explain your conclusions using your knowledge of chemistry .

Evaluating the evidence (E)

You need to decide how well the investigation went. This account should include answers to the following questions:

- Were your results accurate? Do they agree with other results for the same experiment?
- Were your results reliable? If you repeated the experiment, did you get similar results each time?
- Do your results agree with your prediction? If not, is this because the prediction was wrong, or because of a fault in the design of the method?
- How would you improve your experiment if you were to do it again?

Success in examinations

If you have worked hard for two years and put in a lot of effort, there are some steps you can take to ensure that your examination result reflects this.

Be prepared

If the thought of an examination fills you with dread, then you are probably not fully prepared. Of course everybody will be a bit nervous about an important examination, but there is no reason why you should fall apart and fail to do yourself justice if you know what to expect before you go in. The best preparation is working through past papers and looking at your syllabus to avoid any nasty surprises. A positive attitude will help you - try to look on the examination as an opportunity to show the examiner all the things you have learnt in the past two years.

Make sure you have everything you need ready the night before, including pens, pencils, ruler, and calculator. Your teacher can tell you what mathematical skills you are expected to have, or they are listed in your syllabus. Make sure you are familiar with these well in advance.

Read carefully

Before you start, read the paper all the way through and make sure you know exactly what you have to do. Turn over all the pages. Then, when you are ready to start, read each question more than once to make sure it really does say what you think it says. Follow the instructions to the letter, as marks can only be awarded for precise answers to the question asked, not for any other information about the subject.

Plan your time

Work out how much time you should spend on each question, based on how many marks it has. Don't spend ages racking your brains to think of the answer to the last part of a question - go on and start the next question instead. You will probably get more marks for answering the beginning of all the questions than for finishing one or two questions completely, but not attempting later questions. If you have time left at the end, you can go back and think about the more difficult parts when you will be feeling more relaxed.

Present your work clearly

Remember that the examiner will have a large pile of papers to mark in a short space of time. Struggling to read your writing or to follow an illogical argument will not help, so write as clearly as you possibly can in the time available and think through what you are going to write before you start. The examiner is trying to award you marks - make it easy to find them.

If you are drawing diagrams, draw them clearly and simply, using single lines where appropriate. Label the diagrams and make sure the label lines point exactly to the relevant structures.

Stay calm

If you find a question you have no idea about, do not panic! Breathe slowly and deeply and have another look. It's likely that if you stay calm and think clearly, it will start to make more sense, or at least you may be able to answer part of it. If not, then don't agonise about it but concentrate first on the questions you *can* answer.

Exam Organisation Addresses

EDEXCEL (formerly ULEAC)
Stewart House, 32 Russell Square, LONDON WC1B 5DN
Tel: 0171 331 4000   Fax: 0171 331 4044

Midland Examining Group (MEG) and International General Certificate of Education (IGCSE)
Head office, Syndicate Buildings, 1 Hills Road, CAMBRIDGE CB1 2EU
Tel: 01223 553311   Fax: 01223 460278

Northern Examining and Assessment Board (NEAB)
Head office, Devas Street, Manchester M15 6EX
Tel: 0161 953 1180   Fax: 0161 273 7572

Northern Ireland Council for the Curriculum, Examinations and Assessment (CCEA)
Beechill House, 42 Beechill Road,
BELFAST BT8 4RS
Tel: 01232 704666   Fax: 01232 799913

Southern Examining Group (SEG)
Associated Examining Board, Stag Hill House, GUILDFORD, Surrey GU2 5XJ
Tel: 01483 506506   Fax: 01483 300152

Welsh Joint Education Committee (WJEC)
Welsh Joint Education Committee, 245 Western Avenue, CARDIFF CF5 2YX
Tel: 01222 265000   Fax: 01222 575895

How to revise

You will probably have found by talking to other pupils that everybody has a different way of revising. It's important to make sure that your method is an effective one.

Make a revision timetable

First plan your revision. You have a lot of subjects to fit in, but you *can* cover them all, and keep up with your hobbies too, if you plan your time carefully. A blank revision timetable is provided on page x. Make a timetable that includes all your subjects, and think about combining the subjects you find difficult with those that come more naturally to you, so you have something to look forward to and don't get disheartened. Use your syllabus to make sure you have covered everything. Once you've made the timetable, though, make sure you really do start revising - don't kid yourself that planning your revision is all you need to do!

Find a suitable place to revise

You need somewhere quiet where you will not be interrupted. Some people can concentrate with music playing, but if you can't, then turn it off. If you find it difficult to work at home, then try going to a library or some other quiet place.

Work with the material

Don't just sit there reading. You need to interact or work with the main ideas to get them fixed in your mind, rather than just trying to learn reams of words on a page. Different people do this in various ways, but you could try the following:

- if this book is your own, using a highlighter pen to show key words

- making brief notes, or reorganising your own notes

- organising the information in different ways, such as making lists or flow diagrams, or using coloured highlighters to code related information

- drawing pictures or making up mnemonics or rhymes to help you remember key facts or important ideas

- reading a section and then testing yourself.

Try working with a friend, and don't forget to ask your teacher for advice if you get stuck.

Take regular breaks

Your concentration will start to wander and you will be less effective if you work solidly for hours without a break. Divide up your study periods into chunks of about 40 minutes, and then go and make a drink, or have a brief walk, or do something completely different for about 10 minutes. Then you can go back for the next session feeling refreshed, and sometimes you will find that you understand things more clearly after a break.

Go over topics repeatedly

You can fix things in your memory most effectively if you go back over them regularly. Each time you start a revision session, briefly go over or test yourself on some of the things you have learnt earlier. The more times you think about a topic, the more likely you are to remember it, even when under pressure in an examination.

Work through past examination papers

It's important not only to learn the information, but also to be able to answer the sorts of questions that are likely to come up. There is more about this on page vi.

Don't panic at the last minute

If you have stuck to your revision timetable, you should feel as relaxed and confident as you can about the examination. There is then no point in panicking and trying to learn it all again the night before. Just have a quick look through your brief notes, diagrams or lists, test yourself on a couple of topics, and then relax. If you are nervous and feel convinced you have forgotten everything, then take some exercise or do something else to clear your thoughts and stop worrying. You will probably find that when you come back and have another look, you have remembered far more than you thought.

Revision Timetable

Date						
Day	Monday	Tuesday	Wednesday	Thursday	Friday	Saturday	Sunday
Subject/Topic						
Time/Comments						
Date						
Day	Monday	Tuesday	Wednesday	Thursday	Friday	Saturday	Sunday
Subject/Topic						
Time/Comments						
Date						
Day	Monday	Tuesday	Wednesday	Thursday	Friday	Saturday	Sunday
Subject/Topic						
Time/Comments						
Date						
Day	Monday	Tuesday	Wednesday	Thursday	Friday	Saturday	Sunday
Subject/Topic						
Time/Comments						
Date						
Day	Monday	Tuesday	Wednesday	Thursday	Friday	Saturday	Sunday
Subject/Topic						
Time/Comments						

Matter and energy

MATTER

Matter makes up all the substances around us.

Matter can be recognized by weighing because it has mass.

Matter exists in three **states**: **solid**, **liquid**, and **gas**.

When the particles of a substance gain or lose energy, the substance may change state.

Melting and boiling points

These are **temperatures at which pure substances change state**.

They are used by chemists to:
- recognize substances: no two substances have exactly the same melting or boiling points;
- check purity: impurities change melting and boiling points.

Sublimation

This is the process of turning directly from solid to gas (instead of melting to a liquid).

Iodine and carbon dioxide (dry ice) both sublime.

Gas

sublimation point

Solid

ENERGY

Energy is the ability to do work.

Energy of *movement* is called **kinetic energy**, e.g. energy of a moving ball.

Energy of *position* is called **potential energy**, e.g. energy of a raised weight.

Other kinds of energy – heat (thermal), sound, light, chemical, nuclear – are all forms of either kinetic or potential energy. They all depend on the movement or position of particles in matter.

The **heat** in a substance is the sum of the kinetic energy of all the particles in the substance.

The **temperature** of a substance is a measure of the kinetic energy of the particles in the substance. In a hot substance the particles have more kinetic energy than in a cold substance.

States of matter

boiling point

freezing point
melting point

Gas
- has a fixed mass: often very small for such a large volume (balloons float)
- has no fixed volume: can be squashed (used in vehicle tyres to cushion bumps)
- has no fixed shape: can be poured (wind)

Diffusion

The particles of a gas are moving all the time. They move so fast and so randomly that they spread out in all directions until they meet the wall of a container. This is why two gases mix completely with each other. The process is called diffusion.

Liquid
- has a fixed mass
- has a fixed volume: cannot be squashed (used in hydraulic systems)
- has no fixed shape: can be poured (flows along pipes)

Solid
- has a fixed mass
- has a fixed volume
- has a fixed shape: solids are used to build structures

Solids may be either:
- **crystalline**, when they have been cooled slowly:
  the particles have time to form an ordered lattice, or
- **amorphous** (powder), when they have been cooled quickly:
  the particles do not have time to get arranged into a pattern.

THE INTERACTION OF MATTER AND ENERGY

In chemistry we study the effects of applying energy to matter or getting matter to release stored energy.

In chemical plants energy, heat, and pressure are applied to raw materials like crude oil or iron ore, changing them into useful substances that we need.

In power stations fuels react with air. The potential energy stored in the fuel (in the bonds between the atoms) is released as kinetic (heat) energy which is made to do work generating electricity.

Changing state and the kinetic theory

① When a gas is cooled, its temperature falls until it reaches its boiling point.
② It then begins to condense into a liquid.
③ The temperature does not drop any further until all the gas has condensed.
④ The liquid then cools until it reaches its freezing point.
⑤ It then begins to freeze, forming a solid.
⑥ The temperature does not drop any further until all the liquid has frozen.

This behaviour is shown here on a **cooling curve**, which shows how temperature changes with time. The behaviour is explained using the **kinetic theory**.

The kinetic theory explains the properties of the different states of matter by the behaviour of the particles in the matter. It describes the movement of the particles (the **kinetic energy**) and their relative positions (the **potential energy**).

COOLING CURVE FOR WATER

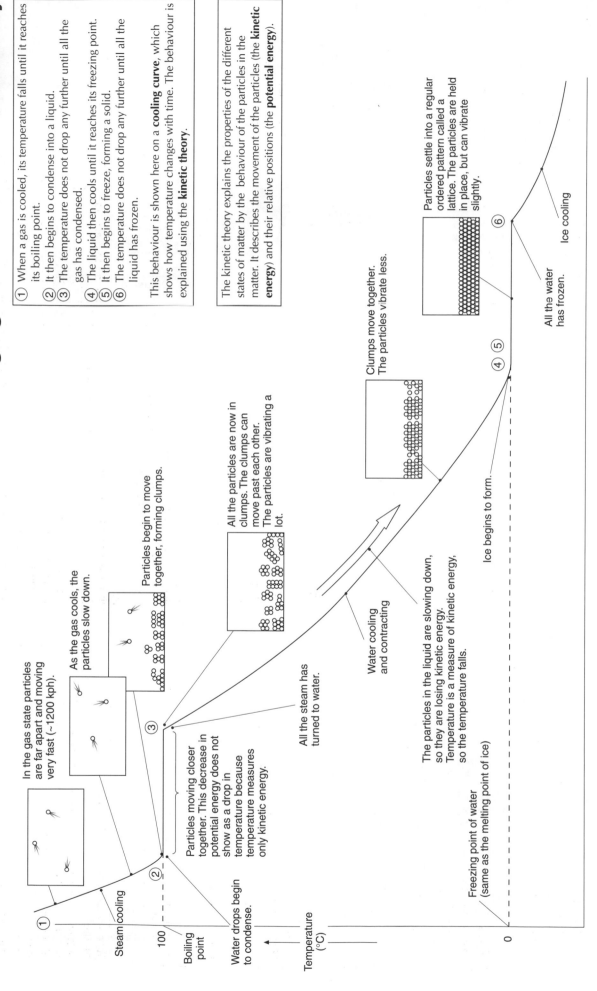

In the gas state particles are far apart and moving very fast (~1200 kph).

As the gas cools, the particles slow down.

Particles begin to move together, forming clumps.

All the particles are now in clumps. The clumps can move past each other. The particles are vibrating a lot.

Clumps move together. The particles vibrate less.

Particles settle into a regular ordered pattern called a lattice. The particles are held in place, but can vibrate slightly.

Steam cooling

Particles moving closer together. This decrease in potential energy does not show as a drop in temperature because temperature measures only kinetic energy.

All the steam has turned to water.

Water cooling and contracting

The particles in the liquid are slowing down, so they are losing kinetic energy. Temperature is a measure of kinetic energy, so the temperature falls.

Ice begins to form.

All the water has frozen.

Ice cooling

Freezing point of water (same as the melting point of ice)

Boiling point

Water drops begin to condense.

Temperature (°C)

100

0

Time

Elements, mixtures, and compounds

ELEMENTS

- cannot be decomposed
- made of only one kind of atom
- two main kinds: metals and non-metals

Metals

Physical properties
- conduct electricity
- ductile and malleable (can be bent and shaped)

Chemical properties
- form basic oxides, e.g. MgO; CuO
- form cations, e.g. Na^+; Ca^{2+}

Non-metals

Physical properties
- insulators
- brittle (suddenly snap when loaded)

Chemical properties
- form acidic oxides, e.g. CO_2; SO_2; NO_2
- form anions, e.g. O^{2-}; Cl^-; Br^-

Relative amounts in Earth's crust

Element	%	
oxygen	46.6	most abundant non-metal
silicon	27.7	
aluminium	8.1	most abundant metal
iron	5.0	
calcium	3.6	
hydrogen	0.22	
carbon	0.19	forms most compounds

IRON FILINGS grey, magnetic

+

SULPHUR yellow, low m.p.

MIX

MIXTURES

- made by physical change
- original properties still remain
- have variable composition
- there is no energy change when mixing
- separated by physical changes
- made from elements or compounds

MIXTURE
Both grey iron filings and yellow sulphur can still be seen; separate with magnet.

Important examples

Air
- mixture of gases
- main components

nitrogen	78%
oxygen	21%
noble gases	0.9%
carbon dioxide	0.04%

- separated by fractional distillation

Petroleum
- mixture of saturated hydrocarbons
- composition changes from one source to another
- separated by fractional distillation

Sea water
- mixture of ionic salts in water

Salt	Mass (g in 100g of sea water)
sodium chloride	2.6
magnesium chloride	0.3
magnesium sulphate	0.2
calcium sulphate	0.1
potassium chloride	0.1

- separated by distillation to collect water, and evaporation to collect salt.

COMBINE

COMPOUNDS

- made by chemical change
- have new properties, different from reactants
- have fixed composition and definite formula
- there is an energy change during combination
- can only be separated by decomposition (a chemical change)

COMPOUND

Black lump of non-magnetic iron(II) sulphide

Exothermic reaction: mixture glows red hot once the heat energy starts the reaction.

Important examples

water	H_2O
ammonia	NH_3
methane	CH_4
carbon dioxide	CO_2
sodium chloride	$NaCl$
calcium carbonate	$CaCO_3$
iron oxide	Fe_2O_3

Mixtures

- made of more than one substance
- have variable composition
- properties are those of the original substances added together
- no energy change when mixing happens

SOLUTIONS

Recognized by being transparent – you can see through them.

The **solute** is the smaller part of the solution, often a solid.

The **solvent** is the larger part of a solution, usually a liquid.

Solutions are described as **homogeneous** or **uniform mixtures**.

Both the solute and solvent particles are very small and nearly the same size, so they are all in the same state or phase.

Important examples of solutions

Air

A mixture of gases. Nitrogen (~78%) is the solvent. Oxygen (~21%), the noble gases, and carbon dioxide are some of the solutes. The b.p.s are very close, so air is separated by fractional distillation:

nitrogen boils at –196°C
oxygen boils at –183°C

Nitrogen boils first and comes off the top of the column. Oxygen is left at the bottom.

Crude oil

A mixture of saturated hydrocarbons. Composition varies and all the boiling points are very close together. So it is separated into **fractions**, which are groups of hydrocarbons with similar boiling points.

Sea water

Sea water is evaporated to provide common salt (sodium chloride) and the other solutes it contains. In dry parts of the world it is used to provide water for drinking and irrigation. The sea water is distilled, or separated by a process called reverse osmosis.

SUSPENSIONS

Recognized by being opaque – you cannot see through them.

Here the particles which are suspended are much larger than the particles they are suspended in. The suspended particles are actually clumps of pure solid or liquid. They are big enough to reflect light, so the mixture is opaque. Because these big particles are in a different state from the smaller particles, suspensions are called **heterogeneous** or **non-uniform mixtures**.

Often the larger particles sink to the bottom and the suspension separates by itself, but this can take a long time.

Important examples of suspensions

Milk
Particles of fat are suspended in water. They are less dense than water and in time will rise to the top (look at a bottle of full-cream milk).

Emulsion paint
Particles of coloured pigment are suspended in water. They settle to the bottom if the paint has not been stirred for a long time.

Muddy water
Mud particles are suspended when the water is stirred up. But the mud will settle out if the water is left undisturbed.

Salad dressing
Oil particles are suspended in the vinegar when the dressing is shaken. When left to stand the oil and vinegar separate into two layers.

Separating mixtures

SOLUTIONS

Because all the particles are in the same state, solutions can only be separated by making one part change state.

Evaporation

Evaporation is used to collect the solute. The solvent changes into a gas and leaves the mixture.

Evaporate in a basin with a large surface area on a water bath to prevent overheating and decomposition of the solute.

Distillation

Distillation is used to collect the solvent. The solvent is collected and condensed as it leaves the mixture.

Remember the thermometer. This tells you the boiling point of the solvent, so you can check its identity.

Fractional distillation

This is used when b.p.s are close together. In the fractionating column the vapour condenses and boils many times. Each time the liquid with the lower boiling point gains on the other one and gets to the top first.

Chromatography

This is used when there are many solutes or very small quantities of solute.

Each solute will vary in solubility and in how strongly it bonds to the paper or material in the column. The solute which is most soluble and least well-bonded will travel fastest. So each solute is separated from the others by the process. Solutes can be identified by looking at how far they travel.

SUSPENSIONS

Suspensions are usually easier to separate than solutions because the suspended particles are in a different state. Suspensions can be separated by trapping the larger particles. This is done:
- in filter paper or in a bed of sand
- by careful decanting
- using a tap or separation funnel

Centrifuging

If a suspension is spun very fast, the larger particles move to the outside. So suspensions can be separated by suspending tubes in a centrifuge and spinning them. The residue packs down at the bottom of the tube and the filtrate (liquid) can be poured off.

Filtering

Suspended particles are trapped on the filter paper forming the **residue**. The smaller particles pass through the filter paper forming the **filtrate**.

Using a tap funnel

Two insoluble (**immiscible**) liquids can be separated by running off the lower layer.

Decanting

If the suspension has separated out, the top layer can be carefully poured off.

Atomic structure

The nuclear atom is made of a central part called the nucleus surrounded by an outer part.

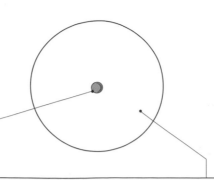

NUCLEUS

- very *small*: less than 0.1% of the volume
- very *massive*: contains 99.9% of the matter
- so *very, very dense*

Contains particles called:

    protons: relative mass 1 unit; relative charge +1 unit

and   **neutrons**: relative mass 1 unit; charge 0

Atomic number
The atomic number of an element is the *number of protons in the atoms of that element.*

Mass number
The mass number of an atom is the *sum of the protons and neutrons in the nucleus of an atom.*

All the atoms of an element have the same atomic number.

ISOTOPES
The number of neutrons in the atoms of an element can vary.

Atoms with the same atomic number but different mass numbers are called **isotopes**.

e.g. there are three isotopes of hydrogen

protium
written as ^1_1H

deuterium
written as ^2_1H

tritium
written as ^3_1H

In the nucleus:

- • = proton

- ○ = neutron

So when writing the symbol for an isotope, write the mass number on top and the atomic number underneath.

THE OUTSIDE

- makes up 99.9% of the volume of the atom
- contains *hardly any mass* (about 0.1%), so is mainly empty space
- is *negatively charged*

Contains particles called **electrons**.

Electrons have very little mass – about 1840 times less than a proton or neutron.

Electrons are negatively charged with a relative charge of –1 unit.

The charge on one electron cancels out the charge on one proton.

Shells
Electrons are arranged around the nucleus in groups called shells.

The shells are numbered starting at the centre and working outwards.

The maximum number of electrons in each shell differs:

    the *first* shell can hold up to **2**
    the *second* shell can hold up to **8**
    the *third* shell can hold up to **8**

ELECTRONIC STRUCTURE
The energy of the electrons in each shell increases with the distance from the nucleus. So electrons in the inner shell have less energy than those in the shells outside. The electrons in each atom go into the shells with the lowest energy, so the inner shells are always filled up first.

The electronic structure (**electronic configuration**) of an atom is the arrangement of the electrons around the nucleus of the atom. It is shown using either a diagram or a list of numbers.

It is worked out like this:
1. Look up the atomic number: this gives you the number of protons. In the neutral atom, the number of electrons is the same as the number of protons.

2. Start filling the shells until the right number of electrons have been placed.

e.g. **fluorine, atomic number 9**
so 2 electrons in the first shell
and 7 electrons in the second shell
written as **2.7**
drawn as

e.g. **magnesium, atomic number 12**
so 2 electrons in the first shell
and 8 electrons in the second shell
and 2 electrons in the third shell
written as **2.8.2**

drawn as

Atomic structure and the periodic table

The arrangement of electrons in an atom – the electronic structure or electronic configuration – is related to the position of the element in the periodic table. The electronic structure for the first three rows of elements is shown below.

Going *across a period* in the table, the atoms of each successive element have *one more outer electron*.

							He
Li	Be	B	C	N	O	F	Ne
Na	Mg	Al	Si	P	S	Cl	Ar

H

First period
1 shell of electrons

Second period
2 shells of electrons

Third period
3 shells of electrons

Group 1	Group 2	Group 3	Group 4	Group 5	Group 6	Group 7	Group 0
Li	Be	B	C	N	O	F	Ne
Na	Mg	Al	Si	P	S	Cl	Ar
One outer electron	Two outer electrons	Three outer electrons	Four outer electrons	Five outer electrons	Six outer electrons	Seven outer electrons	Full shells either 2 or 8 outer electrons

He

The electronic structure of the atom of any element determines its position in the periodic table. For example, sulphur

• is in the *third period* because it has *three shells* of electrons;
• is in group *six* because it has *six* outer electrons.

So the electronic structure of sulphur is: 2.8.6.

Group 6

three shells

TWO KINDS OF ATOM

Metal atoms

Atoms of metallic elements are large and attract outer electrons weakly.
e.g. sodium atom

Non-metal atoms

Atoms of non-metallic elements are smaller and attract outer electrons more strongly.
e.g. chlorine atom

Introduction to bonding and structure

BONDING

A **bond** is any attractive force between particles.

In every bond, positive particles are attracting negative ones.

If electrons are lost by one atom and gained by another, then the two atoms become oppositely charged and a bond forms.

If electrons are shared between two atoms, then the protons in both atoms attract the shared electrons and another kind of bond forms.

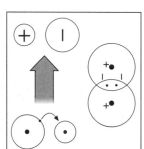

The periodic table helps us decide on the kind of bond

NON-METALS

METALS

If both atoms are *metallic*, the bond is a *metallic* bond, e.g. in copper or aluminium.

If one atom is *metallic* and the other is *non-metallic*, the bond is *ionic*, e.g. in sodium chloride.

If both atoms are *non-metallic*, the bond is *covalent*, e.g. in carbon dioxide, water, or iodine.

Some compounds like sodium hydroxide have two types of bonding: ionic bonding between the sodium ion and the hydroxide ion, and covalent bonding between the hydrogen and oxygen atoms.

Bond strength

There is no simple rule about which types of bonds are strongest.

Metallic bonds vary from the weak ones in mercury to the very strong ones in tungsten.

Ionic and covalent bonds also vary in strength.

STRUCTURE

After bonding takes place, there are different kinds of particle:

Atoms

- Metals are made of giant lattices of atoms held together by metallic bonds.
- Carbon (diamond or graphite) lattices are made of giant lattices of atoms covalently bonded together.
- Noble gas lattices (only formed at very low temperatures) are made of atoms held together by weak van der Waals' forces.

Ions

Compounds made from metals and non-metals exist in giant lattices made of ions. Ions are atoms which have gained or lost electrons and so have a charge.

Cations (metal ions) have positive charges because they have lost electrons.

Anions (non-metal ions) have negative charges because they have gained extra electrons.

Molecules

Elements and compounds of non-metals exist as groups of atoms covalently bonded together. These are called **molecules**. Molecules, like atoms, have no charge.

A **diatomic molecule** is made from only two atoms, e.g. H_2; N_2; O_2; Cl_2; I_2.

A **triatomic molecule** is made from three atoms, e.g. H_2O; CO_2.

Polyatomic molecules are made from many atoms, e.g. CH_4; CH_3CH_2OH.

Bonding between molecules

Just as there are attractive forces between oppositely charged parts of next door atoms, there are also attractive forces between oppositely charged parts of next door molecules.

There are different kinds of forces between molecules. Some are called **polar forces** and some are called **van der Waals' forces**.

The most important thing to remember about these are:

- the forces inside molecules are much stronger than the forces between molecules
- the bigger the molecules are, the stronger the forces between them.

strong bond inside

weak force between

Bonding and structure in metals

A theory of bonding must explain the properties of the substances.

KEY METALLIC PROPERTIES
- good electrical conductivity
- malleable and ductile (can be bent and reshaped without suddenly snapping)

STRUCTURE IN METALS

In most metals the lattice of particles is arranged in the close-packed pattern shown below.

The lattice is formed of cations made of the nucleus and inner shell electrons. So the charge on the cations is always equal to the number of the group of the periodic table that the element is found in.

Between the cations there is a sea of outer electrons. These outer electrons are shared among all the atoms and can move anywhere in the lattice (they are **delocalized**).

Calcium (Group 2) lattice

Sea of delocalized electrons

Aluminium (Group 3) lattice

BONDING IN METALS

Remember that metal atoms are large and attract outer electrons weakly.

In a metal, next door atoms overlap because the outer part of the atoms is mostly empty space.

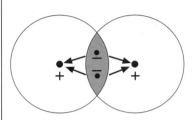

Both nuclei attract the electrons in the overlap area, so there is an attractive force between the atoms called a metallic bond.

Metallic bond: the electrostatic force of attraction that two neighbouring nuclei have for the shared electrons between them.

EXPLAINING THE KEY PROPERTIES

Electrical conductivity
Conduction is the movement of charge. In metals the delocalized electrons drift through the metal lattice carrying the charge.

Malleability and ductility
The shape of metals can be changed because the layers of atoms can slide past or over each other. When they do this, some bonds are broken, but an equal number are made.

CHANGING METALLIC PROPERTIES

Alloying
An alloy is a mixture of a metal and another element. Adding another element disturbs the pattern in the lattice so that the layers will not slide past each other so easily. Alloys are usually stronger and harder than the pure metal.

Heat treatment
If a liquid metal is cooled quickly, the crystals or grains in it have little time to grow. But if it is cooled slowly, large crystals or grains can grow. The crystal or grain size affects the strength of the metal. Metals with larger grains are softer than metals with smaller grains.

If a solid metal is slowly heated to red heat (so that the atoms have enough energy to rearrange) and then is suddenly cooled, the atoms are trapped in a new pattern. The strength and hardness of the metal will be changed.

Uses of metals
The physical properties of metals make them suitable for particular purposes:
- **electrical conduction**: copper and aluminium cables
- **thermal or heat conduction**: copper bottoms to saucepans
- **malleability**: copper pipes, steel car bodies, lead roofs, etc.

Bonding and structure in ionic compounds

A theory of bonding must explain the properties of the substances.

KEY IONIC PROPERTIES

- hard, high melting point solids
- insulators when solid, but conduct when molten or dissolved
- brittle – they break suddenly under load

BONDING IN IONIC COMPOUNDS

Remember that metal atoms are large and hold outer electrons weakly, but non-metal atoms are small and hold outer electrons strongly.

This means that when metal and non-metal atoms meet, electrons are lost by the metal atom and gained by the non-metal atom.

The metal atom loses the outer electrons leaving a positive ion.

The number of electrons lost is the number of electrons in the outer shell. This is the same as the group number, so the charge on the positive ion equals the group number.

e.g. Group   1   2   3
             Na^+ Mg^{2+} Al^{3+}

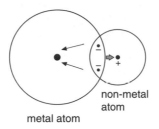

metal atom   non-metal atom

The non-metal atom gains new outer electrons making a negative ion.

Electrons are gained from the metal atom until the outer shell is full. So the charge on the ion is the same as the number of gaps in the outer shell. This is given by (8 – group number).

e.g. Group   6   7   0
            O^{2-} F^- –

                  no gaps so no ions formed

For example, when sodium and chlorine react:

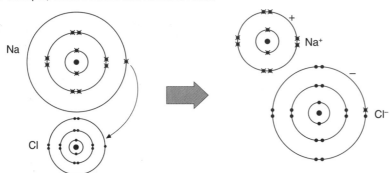

The ions formed have full outer shells. They have the same electronic structure as a noble gas.

The oppositely charged ions attract each other and an ionic bond is formed.

Ionic bond: the electrostatic force of attraction between two oppositely charged ions formed as the result of electron transfer. Ionic bonds are sometimes called electrovalent bonds.

STRUCTURE IN IONIC COMPOUNDS

The oppositely charged ions clump together and a lattice forms. When you draw an ionic lattice, do not draw lines between the ions: lines are used to represent covalent bonds. Remember that positive ions are nearly always smaller than negative ones.

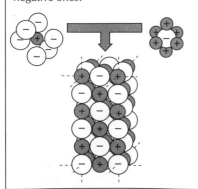

EXPLAINING THE KEY PROPERTIES

Hardness, high melting point
Oppositely charged ions attract each other strongly forming a lattice which is difficult to break up.

Electrical properties
In the solid state the ions are held in place and cannot move. Once the substance has melted or dissolved, the ions can move and carry charge. Positive ions are attracted towards the cathode: they are called cations. Negative ions are attracted towards the anode: they are called anions.

Brittleness
When a force is applied, the strongly bonded lattice resists. But eventually the layers start to slide past each other. Ions of the same charge move next to each other and repulsion replaces attraction. The solid breaks.

Current flows and light glows when lead(II) bromide melts

Bonding in covalent substances

A theory of bonding must explain the properties of substances.

KEY COVALENT PROPERTIES

There are two different kinds of covalent substance:
- *either* gases, liquids, and soft solids, *or*
- hard, very high m.p. solids

Both are insulators.
Both are brittle in the solid state.

Covalent bonding is found in non-metallic elements as well as compounds.

BONDING IN COVALENT SUBSTANCES

Remember that non-metal atoms are smaller than metal ones and attract their electrons strongly.

When two non-metal atoms touch and overlap, pairs of electrons in the area of overlap get attracted to both nuclei and a bond forms.

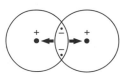

Covalent bond: the electrostatic force of attraction that two nuclei have for a shared pair of electrons between them.

A covalent bond can be drawn in a number of ways. For example, the bond between two hydrogen atoms can be drawn in three ways.

H:H   or   H×H   or   H — H

NUMBER OF BONDS FORMED

The number of covalent bonds an atom of an element makes depends on the position of the element in the periodic table.

Remember that to make a covalent bond an atom needs
- an electron to put into the bond, and
- a space or gap in its outer shell into which the other atom's electron can go.

The table shows this.

Group	3	4	5	6	7	8
Number of electrons in outer shell	3	4	5	6	7	8
Number of gaps in outer shell	5	4	3	2	1	0
Number of bonds made	3	4	3	2	1	0
Examples	Cl. ×B:Cl Cl	H H:C:H H	H:N:H	H:O: H	H:Cl:	:Ne:

All these molecules have one or more shared pairs of electrons making the bonds. Some of them also have pairs of electrons belonging to one atom only. These are called **non-bonding pairs** or **lone pairs**.

DOUBLE AND TRIPLE BONDING

Sometimes atoms can share more than one pair of electrons between them. When this happens, double or even triple bonds are made.

in oxygen, O_2

in carbon dioxide, CO_2 lone pairs can be shown like this

in ethene, C_2H_4

in nitrogen, N_2

It does not matter whether the bonds made are single, double, or triple: the total number of bonds made by an atom does not change. In the examples here, carbon still makes four bonds, nitrogen makes three, oxygen makes two, and hydrogen makes one.

Structure of covalent substances

MOLECULAR COVALENT SUBSTANCES

These substances exist as separate, covalently bonded molecules. Molecules have no charge.

The covalent bonding *inside* each molecule is *very strong*, but the bonding *between* the molecules is much, much *weaker*. It is this weak bonding which is overcome when these substances are broken or melted.

The solid lattices are made of ordered arrangements of molecules.

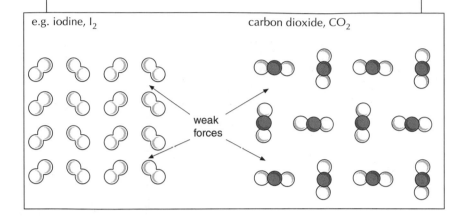

e.g. iodine, I$_2$ carbon dioxide, CO$_2$

weak forces

EXPLAINING THE KEY PROPERTIES

Softness and low melting point
When a force is applied to these substances, or when they are heated, it is the weak forces *between* the molecules that are overcome. The strong forces inside the molecules are not overcome.

Because these intermolecular (between molecules) forces are so weak, the solids are soft and melt easily.

Insulators
There are no charged particles free to move in these substances. The electrons are localized in pairs and there are no ions. So they do not conduct.

Brittleness
When force is applied and the weak forces are overcome, no new bonds are made. The substance suddenly breaks.

MACROMOLECULAR (GIANT COVALENT) SUBSTANCES

These substances exist in huge, covalently bonded lattices. A diamond is a single giant molecule with millions of bonds. Strong covalent bonding continues throughout the whole lattice. Here there are no weak forces to break, only strong covalent bonds.

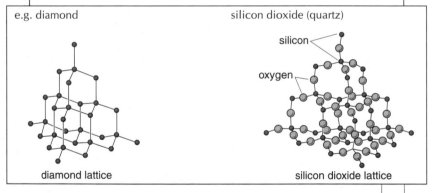

e.g. diamond   silicon dioxide (quartz)

silicon

oxygen

diamond lattice   silicon dioxide lattice

EXPLAINING THE KEY PROPERTIES

Hardness and high melting point
Breaking or melting these substances involves breaking strong covalent bonds. So these substances are very hard with very high m.p.s. Diamond is the hardest substance known.

Insulators
There are no charged particles free to move in these substances. The electrons are localized in pairs and there are no ions. So they do not conduct.

Brittleness
When force is applied and the weak forces are overcome, no new bonds are made. The substance suddenly breaks.

THE UNUSUAL PROPERTIES OF GRAPHITE

Graphite is a form of carbon. Although it is covalently bonded, it conducts electricity. Carbon rods used for electrolysis are made of graphite.

Graphite has a layered structure in which each carbon uses only three electrons for bonding. The fourth electron from each atom is delocalized and shared throughout the layer. Because graphite has delocalized electrons (like a metal), it conducts electricity (like a metal).

Carbon atoms also exist in cage-like lattices called fullerenes.

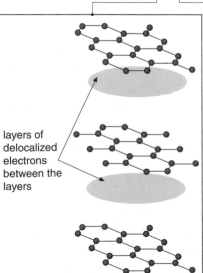

layers of delocalized electrons between the layers

POLYMERS

Polymers are giant chains of covalently bonded atoms forming extremely long molecules. Like other covalent molecules, the forces between them are much weaker than the forces inside them. But these long molecules can tangle together like string or spaghetti. This tangling is made worse if the polymer molecules have side chains sticking out of them.

Plastics are polymers. Some plastics are bendy and flexible because of this tangling of long polymer chains.

Tangled chains

Bonding and structure in the main groups of the periodic table

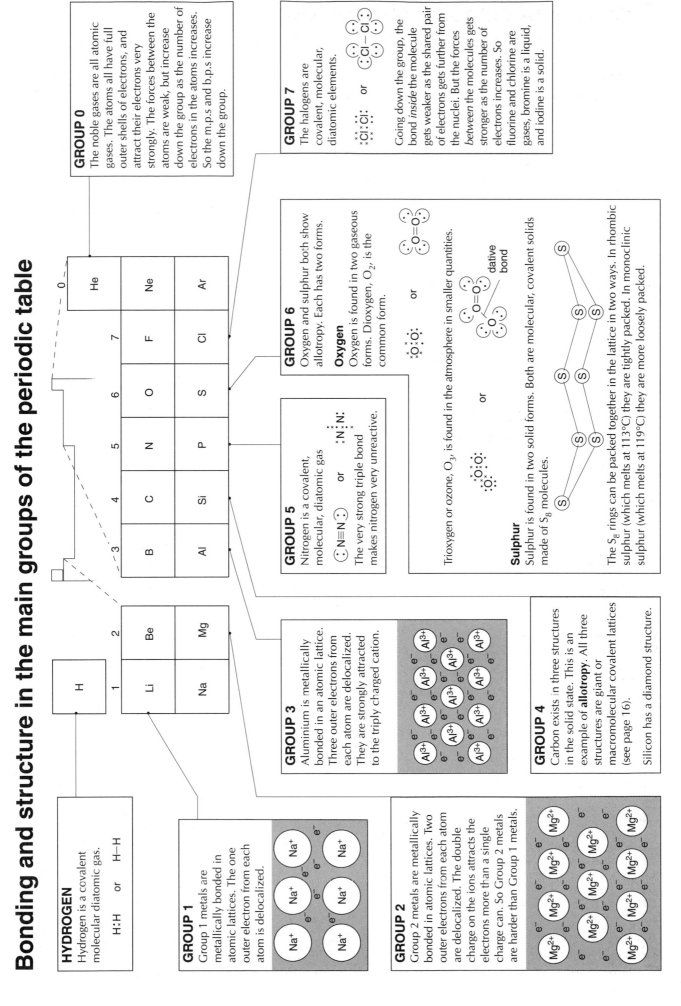

HYDROGEN

Hydrogen is a covalent molecular diatomic gas.

H×H   or   H—H

GROUP 1

Group 1 metals are metallically bonded in atomic lattices. The one outer electron from each atom is delocalized.

GROUP 2

Group 2 metals are metallically bonded in atomic lattices. Two outer electrons from each atom are delocalized. The double charge on the ions attracts the electrons more than a single charge can. So Group 2 metals are harder than Group 1 metals.

GROUP 3

Aluminium is metallically bonded in an atomic lattice. Three outer electrons from each atom are delocalized. They are strongly attracted to the triply charged cation.

GROUP 4

Carbon exists in three structures in the solid state. This is an example of **allotropy**. All three structures are giant or macromolecular covalent lattices (see page 16).

Silicon has a diamond structure.

GROUP 5

Nitrogen is a covalent, molecular, diatomic gas.

The very strong triple bond makes nitrogen very unreactive.

GROUP 6

Oxygen and sulphur both show allotropy. Each has two forms.

Oxygen

Oxygen is found in two gaseous forms. Dioxygen, O_2, is the common form.

dative bond

Trioxygen or ozone, O_3, is found in the atmosphere in smaller quantities.

Sulphur

Sulphur is found in two solid forms. Both are molecular, covalent solids made of S_8 molecules.

The S_8 rings can be packed together in the lattice in two ways. In rhombic sulphur (which melts at 113°C) they are tightly packed. In monoclinic sulphur (which melts at 119°C) they are more loosely packed.

GROUP 7

The halogens are covalent, molecular, diatomic elements.

Going down the group, the bond *inside* the molecule gets weaker as the shared pair of electrons gets further from the nuclei. But the forces *between* the molecules gets stronger as the number of electrons increases. So fluorine and chlorine are gases, bromine is a liquid, and iodine is a solid.

GROUP 0

The noble gases are all atomic gases. The atoms all have full outer shells of electrons, and attract their electrons very strongly. The forces between the atoms are weak, but increase down the group as the number of electrons in the atoms increases. So the m.p.s and b.p.s increase down the group.

The periodic table

The periodic table is a list of the elements in order of their atomic numbers.

The list is set out so that elements with similar properties are in vertical columns.

GROUPS

- The long vertical columns of elements are called **groups**.
- The groups are numbered from 0 to 7.
- A group contains elements with similar properties.
- Going down a group, the elements show trends as the properties they share change slightly.

Hydrogen is the first element and is unlike any other. So hydrogen is in a box by itself and is not part of any of the groups.

GROUP NAMES

Some groups have names as well as numbers.

- Group 0 is called the **noble gases**.
- Group 1 is called the **alkali metals**.
- Group 2 is called the **alkaline earth metals**.
- Group 7 is called the **halogens**.

PERIODS

Periods are horizontal rows of elements. A period contains elements with different properties. Each period, apart from the first one, starts with metals and changes to non-metals.

TRANSITION ELEMENTS

This is a large collection of elements between Groups 2 and 3. The elements in the main groups differ in properties from group to group. But the transition elements all have certain properties in common:

1. **They are metals with high m.p. and density** (Titanium is exceptional in being very light, zinc is exceptional in melting at a low temperature.)
2. **The elements and their compounds often act as catalysts** e.g. iron in the Haber process, vanadium(V) oxide in the Contact process, nickel in margarine manufacture.
3. **They form coloured compounds** e.g. potassium manganate(VII) is purple; potassium dichromate is orange; iron(II) sulphate is green; iron(III) nitrate is brown; copper(II) sulphate is blue.
4. **They can react with another element to form more than one compound** e.g. copper forms two oxides, copper(I) oxide, Cu_2O, and copper(II) oxide, CuO; iron forms two chlorides, iron(II) chloride, $FeCl_2$, and iron(III) chloride, $FeCl_3$.

METALS AND NON-METALS

The simplest way to divide up the periodic table is into metallic and non-metallic elements.

The *metals* appear on the *left* of the zig-zag line, while the *non-metals* are on the *right* of the line. You can see that there are many more metals than non-metals.

METALLOIDS OR SEMI-METALS

Elements near the zig-zag line often show some metallic properties and some non-metallic properties. For example:

- carbon (graphite) is a non-metal, but conducts electricity
- silicon and germanium are called **semiconductors** and have resistances which change markedly with conditions
- aluminium oxide has both basic and acidic properties (**amphoteric**).

transition elements

Group 1

All the elements in this group
- are soft, silvery metals
- are very reactive (they are kept under oil to stop them reacting with air or water)
- form ions with a single positive charge

Going down the group
- melting points decrease
- reactivity increases

The reason for both these trends is the same. The attraction of the nucleus for the outer electron gets less as the atoms get bigger going down the group. So the metallic bond is weaker, and the atoms lose the outer electron more easily.

Li⁺ Na⁺ K⁺

Ions formed   Outer electrons getting further from nucleus

Reaction with water
The metals react with water rapidly in the cold. They make an *alkaline solution* and hydrogen.

e.g. $2Na(s) + 2H_2O(l) \rightarrow 2NaOH(aq) + H_2(g)$

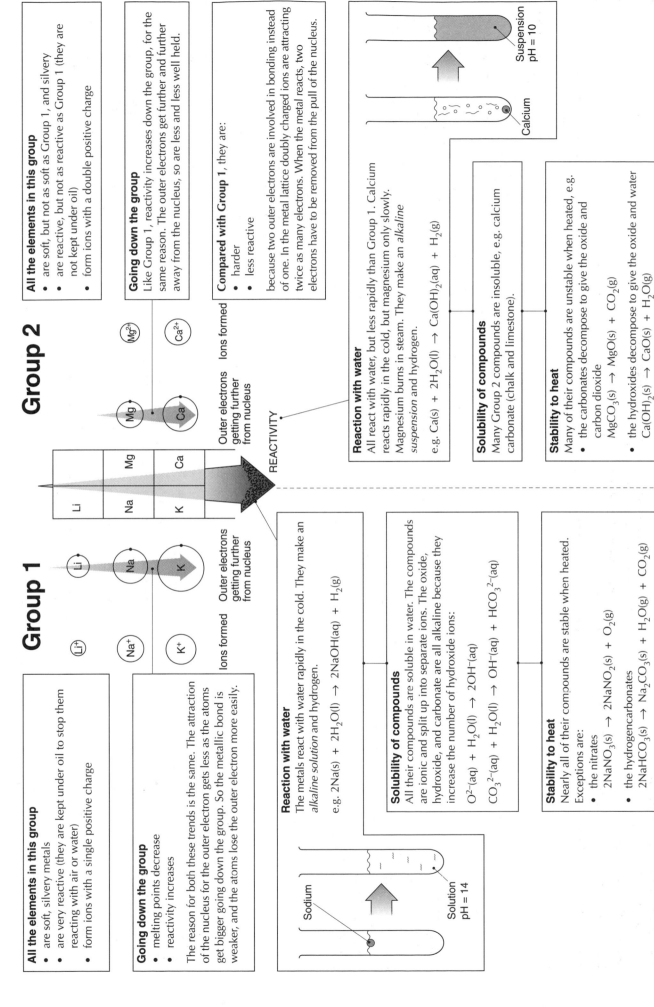

Sodium

Solution pH = 14

Solubility of compounds
All their compounds are soluble in water. The compounds are ionic and split up into separate ions. The oxide, hydroxide, and carbonate are all alkaline because they increase the number of hydroxide ions:

$O^{2-}(aq) + H_2O(l) \rightarrow 2OH^-(aq)$

$CO_3^{2-}(aq) + H_2O(l) \rightarrow OH^-(aq) + HCO_3^{2-}(aq)$

Stability to heat
Nearly all of their compounds are stable when heated. Exceptions are:
- the nitrates
  $2NaNO_3(s) \rightarrow 2NaNO_2(s) + O_2(g)$
- the hydrogencarbonates
  $2NaHCO_3(s) \rightarrow Na_2CO_3(s) + H_2O(g) + CO_2(g)$

Group 2

All the elements in this group
- are soft, but not as soft as Group 1, and silvery
- are reactive, but not as reactive as Group 1 (they are not kept under oil)
- form ions with a double positive charge

Going down the group
Like Group 1, reactivity increases down the group, for the same reason. The outer electrons get further and further away from the nucleus, so are less and less well held.

Compared with Group 1, they are:
- harder
- less reactive

because two outer electrons are involved in bonding instead of one. In the metal lattice doubly charged ions are attracting twice as many electrons. When the metal reacts, two electrons have to be removed from the pull of the nucleus.

Mg²⁺ Ca²⁺

Outer electrons getting further from nucleus   Ions formed

Mg Ca

REACTIVITY

Li Na K
    Mg Ca

Reaction with water
All react with water, but less rapidly than Group 1. Calcium reacts rapidly in the cold, but magnesium only slowly. Magnesium burns in steam. They make an *alkaline suspension* and hydrogen.

e.g. $Ca(s) + 2H_2O(l) \rightarrow Ca(OH)_2(aq) + H_2(g)$

Calcium

Suspension pH = 10

Solubility of compounds
Many Group 2 compounds are insoluble, e.g. calcium carbonate (chalk and limestone).

Stability to heat
Many of their compounds are unstable when heated, e.g.
- the carbonates decompose to give the oxide and carbon dioxide
  $MgCO_3(s) \rightarrow MgO(s) + CO_2(g)$
- the hydroxides decompose to give the oxide and water
  $Ca(OH)_2(s) \rightarrow CaO(s) + H_2O(g)$

Group 0, the noble gases

All the elements in this group

- are colourless gases
- are found in small amounts in the air
- are very, very unreactive (helium and neon never react, the others only very rarely and under special conditions)

The atoms are relatively small with full shells. They hold on to the electrons they already have strongly and have no room to gain any new electrons

Going down the group

- the elements get more dense
- the boiling points increase

Uses

Their uses depend on their physical properties or their unreactivity.

Helium
- in balloons (very low density)
- for deep diving (unreactive)
- used for super-cooling (low b.p.)

Neon
- in advertising signs (glows in electric field)

Argon
- to fill light bulbs (unreactive and cheap)
- in welding (unreactive)

Xenon
- in flash bulbs (unreactive). The unreactive gas prevents the filament of the bulb reacting when it flashes and gets very hot, so the bulb can be used many times.

0
He
Ne
Ar
Kr
Xe

density →

7
F
Cl
Br
I

← element reactivity

Elements

yellow gas
green gas
red liquid
dark grey solid

Ions

F^-
Cl^-
Br^-
I^-

Group 7, the halogens

All the elements in this group

- are coloured non-metals; the colour darkens down the group.
- exist as **diatomic molecules** (molecules made of two atoms): F_2; Cl_2; Br_2; I_2
- have melting and boiling points which increase down the group
- are very reactive

Going down the group

Reactivity *decreases* down the group, so each halogen displaces the ones below it from their compounds:

e.g.
$Cl_2(g) + 2KBr(aq) \rightarrow Br_2(aq) + 2KCl(aq)$
$Cl_2(g) + 2KI(aq) \rightarrow I_2(aq) + 2KCl(aq)$
$Br_2(g) + 2KI(aq) \rightarrow I_2(aq) + 2KBr(aq)$

This trend in reactivity is opposite to that seen in Groups 1 and 2.

The reason for this is that these elements react by *gaining* electrons instead of losing them like metal atoms do. They usually react to form anions with a *single negative charge*. The smaller atoms at the top of the group attract electrons more strongly than the larger ones at the bottom. So the elements at the top of the group are more reactive than those below them.

Reactions

All the elements in this group
- react with hydrogen forming hydrogen halides which are acidic in water

e.g. $H_2(g) + Cl_2(g) \rightarrow 2HCl(g)$
$HCl(g) + H_2O(l) \rightarrow H_3O^+(aq) + Cl^-(aq)$

- react with metals forming ionic metal halides

e.g. $Na(s) + Cl_2(g) \rightarrow 2NaCl(s)$
$2Al(s) + 3Cl_2(g) \rightarrow 2AlCl_3(s)$

Iron reacts similarly.

Uses

Halogens are very **reactive oxidizing agents**. Solutions of chlorine in water and iodine in alcohol are used to kill bacteria.

Fluoride ions are added to toothpaste; a fluorine compound is the surface on non-stick pans.

Chlorine forms many covalent compounds with many important uses:
- CH_3CCl_3, 1,1,1-trichloroethane, is a very good solvent, used in dry cleaning
- CCl_2F_2, a chlorofluorocarbon (CFC) used as an aerosol propellant, now discontinued because of damage to the ozone layer.

Other compounds are used as anaesthetics, drugs, pesticides, and herbicides.

Precipitation reactions of halide ions

Halide ions in solution react with silver ions to form insoluble precipitates:

$Ag^+(aq) + Cl^-(aq) \rightarrow AgCl(s)$ white
$Ag^+(aq) + Br^-(aq) \rightarrow AgBr(s)$ cream
$Ag^+(aq) + I^-(aq) \rightarrow AgI(s)$ yellow

These solids darken in light and form the basis of photographic film.

SILVER NITRATE

Halide solution

Precipitate of silver halide

Sulphur chemistry

SULPHURIC ACID, H$_2$SO$_4$

Sulphuric acid is probably the most important industrial chemical made because it is used in so many processes. It is made from sulphur in the Contact process.

The Contact process

- sulphur is melted and burnt in air

$$S(l) + O_2(g) \rightarrow SO_2(g)$$

- the sulphur dioxide is oxidized to sulphur trioxide

$$2SO_2(g) + O_2(g) \underset{V_2O_5}{\overset{450°C}{\rightleftharpoons}} 2SO_3(g)$$

- the sulphur trioxide is hydrated with water

$$H_2O(l) + SO_3(g) \rightarrow H_2SO_4(l)$$

Uses

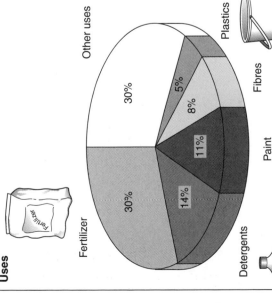

Other uses 30%
Plastics 5%
Fibres 8%
11%
Paint
14%
Detergents
Fertilizer 30%

This is an exothermic combination reaction. The sulphur burns easily and the reaction goes to completion.

This is also an exothermic reaction, but it is reversible.

High rate would be produced by high pressure, high temperature, and a catalyst.

High yield would be produced by high pressure, but low temperature.

The actual conditions used are a compromise.

High pressure is too expensive so a pressure just above atmospheric is used. At 450°C, 97% conversion is achieved.

This is another very exothermic reaction. Just adding the sulphur trioxide gas to water would make the water boil, forming a stable acid mist. To stop this, the sulphur trioxide is bubbled into 98% sulphuric acid, 2% water. This mixture has a much higher boiling point. The water reacts making even more acid without making a mist. So no acid vapours escape from the plant.

SULPHUR

Sulphur is a non-metallic element in Group 6. Its properties are typical of a non-metal.

- **Physical**: brittle, insulating, molecular solid, S$_8$.
- **Chemical**: forms an anion, S^{2-}, and an acidic oxide, SO$_2$.

$$SO_2(g) + H_2O(l) \rightarrow H_2SO_3(aq) \text{ sulphurous acid.}$$

SULPHUR DIOXIDE, SO$_2$

Sulphur dioxide is a covalent, molecular substance, with weak forces between the molecules. It is a dense gas.

It can be oxidized or reduced depending on what it reacts with:

- hydrogen sulphide reduces it to sulphur

$$2H_2S(g) + SO_2(g) \rightarrow 3S(s) + 2H_2O(l)$$

- potassium dichromate oxidizes it in solution; the colour of the dichromate changes from orange to green.

$$K_2Cr_2O_7(aq) + 3H_2SO_3(aq) + H_2SO_4(aq)$$
$$\text{orange}$$
$$\rightarrow Cr_2(SO_4)_3(aq) + K_2SO_4(aq) + 4H_2O(l)$$
$$\text{green}$$

Reactions of concentrated sulphuric acid

- **As a strong acid**

$$H_2SO_4(l) + 2H_2O(l) \rightarrow 2H_3O^+(aq) + SO_4^{2-}(aq)$$

- **As an oxidizing agent**: it will oxidize both metals and non-metals.

$$Cu(s) + 2H_2SO_4(l) \rightarrow CuSO_4(aq) + SO_2(g) + 2H_2O(l)$$
$$C(s) + 2H_2SO_4(l) \rightarrow CO_2(g) + 2SO_2(g) + 2H_2O(l)$$

- **As a dehydrating agent**: it will remove water or the elements of water. It makes hydrated copper(II) sulphate into the anhydrous form

$$CuSO_4.5H_2O(s) \rightarrow CuSO_4(s)$$

It dehydrates sucrose

$$C_{12}H_{22}O_{11}(s) \rightarrow 12C(s)$$

Important ideas about chemical change 1: making new substances

In a chemical reaction

The starting substances – the reactants – react to give new, different substances – the products. The changes which take place in the reaction are usually written as an equation.

$$\text{reactants} \underset{\longleftarrow}{\longrightarrow} \text{products}$$

means 'reacts to give' (sometimes the reaction conditions are written over the arrow)

Word equations

These express in words what is reacting with what to make the products.

e.g. magnesium metal and gaseous oxygen → solid magnesium oxide

Symbol equations

These express in terms of chemical symbols the formulas of the substances taking part in the reaction. They are balanced in the sense that there are the same number of each atom on each side of the arrow.

e.g. $2Mg + O_2 \rightarrow 2MgO$

State symbols

These tell us even more about the reaction. After the formula of each substance there are state symbols which describe the state that the substance is in.

So using (s) for solid, (l) for liquid, (aq) for a solution in water, and (g) for gas, the equation becomes:
$2Mg(s) + O_2(g) \rightarrow 2MgO(s)$

DIFFERENT KINDS OF CHEMICAL CHANGE

Decomposition

Here a single substance is broken down into two or more simpler substances.

e.g. most metal carbonates decompose to give the oxide and carbon dioxide:
$CuCO_3(s) \rightarrow CuO(s) + CO_2(g)$

Remember, substances which cannot be decomposed because they contain only one kind of atom are called elements.

Heat in, so endothermic

Electrolysis

Electrolysis is a form of decomposition. It is used to extract very reactive metals from their ores. The ores of these reactive metals are very stable and cannot be decomposed in any other way.

The metal ions go to the cathode and the non-metal ions go to the anode.

e.g. in molten sodium chloride, the reaction is:
$2NaCl(l)$
$\rightarrow 2Na(l) + Cl_2(g)$

Energy in, so endothermic

Combination

Here two substances (usually elements) react together to make a single new compound.

e.g. metal and non-metal: aluminium and iodine react to give aluminium iodide:
$2Al(s) + 3I_2(s) \rightarrow 2AlI_3(s)$

Sometimes two elements combine together in more than one way.

e.g. carbon can react with oxygen to make two different oxides: carbon monoxide, CO, and carbon dioxide, CO_2. Which one forms depends on how much oxygen is available for the reaction.

Heat out, so exothermic

Displacement

These are reactions in which one element takes the place of another. Both metals and non-metals can do displacements.

More reactive metals can displace less reactive ones from their solutions:
$Fe(s) + CuSO_4(aq) \rightarrow FeSO_4(aq) + Cu(s)$

Reactive metals can displace hydrogen from acids:
$Mg(s) + H_2SO_4(aq) \rightarrow MgSO_4(aq) + H_2(g)$

Very reactive metals can even displace hydrogen from water:
$2Na(s) + 2H_2O(l) \rightarrow 2NaOH(aq) + H_2(g)$

More reactive non-metals can displace less reactive ones from their solutions:
$Cl_2(g) + 2KI(aq) \rightarrow I_2(s) + 2KCl(aq)$

Displacement reactions are a good way of comparing the reactivity of elements.

Important ideas about chemical change 2: energy

EXOTHERMIC CHANGES

The system (the reacting substances) *loses energy to the surroundings.*

e.g. the burning of carbon is an exothermic change.

System — Surroundings

The system loses energy to the surroundings because *less* energy is needed to *break* the bonds in the reactants than to *make* the new bonds in the products.

The energy content of the reactants and products is given the name **enthalpy**. It has the symbol *H*. The difference in enthalpy (the **enthalpy change**) is written mathematically as ΔH and is measured in kilojoules, kJ.

The energy needed to break the bond in the reactant is called the **activation energy**. It has the symbol E_A.

ENDOTHERMIC CHANGES

The system *gains energy from the surroundings.*

e.g. the decomposition of copper carbonate is an endothermic change.

System — Surroundings

The system gains energy from the surroundings because *more* energy is needed to *break* the bonds in the reactants than to *make* the new bonds in the products.

FUELS

Fuels are substances which react exothermically with air making safe products. They combust (burn) easily, so storing them can be a problem.

Hydrogen reacts exothermically and the product (water) is totally safe. But hydrogen is difficult and dangerous to store.

$$2H_2(g) + O_2(g) \longrightarrow 2H_2O(g)$$

Bonds broken	Bonds made	Total energy change
2 H–H = 2 × 436	4 H–O = 4 × 463	
1 O=O = 496		
1368 kJ	1852 kJ	1852 – 1368 = 484 kJ

Methane (natural or North Sea gas) reacts exothermically. The products are carbon dioxide and water. These are safe, although carbon dioxide contributes to global warming.

$$CH_4(g) + 2O_2(g) \longrightarrow CO_2(g) + 2H_2O(g)$$

Bonds broken	Bonds made	Total energy change
4 C–H = 4 × 412	2 C=O = 2 × 743	
2 O=O = 2 × 496	4 H–O = 4 × 463	3338 – 2640
2640	3338	= 698 kJ

Comparing fuels

The most efficient fuel is one that gives out most energy per gram.

4 g of hydrogen produce 484 kJ, so 1 g → 121 kJ
16 g of methane produce 698 kJ, so 1 g → 43.6 kJ

Hydrogen in the more efficient fuel.

FIRE

Fire triangle

For a fire to burn, fuel, air, and heat are needed. The heat provides the **activation energy**, E_A, to break existing bonds.

These three requirements are shown in the fire triangle.

AIR + HEAT ⟹ FIRE
FUEL

REACTANTS + ACTIVATION ENERGY ⟹ REACTION

Preventing or putting out fires

A fire can be prevented by removing any one of the components of the fire triangle:
* remove the air (fire blankets, foam)
* remove the fuel (turn off fuel, use fire breaks in forests)
* remove heat (spray with water)

INCOMPLETE COMBUSTION

In the open air, a fuel reacts with oxygen until it is used up. The fuel is **completely combusted**.

If the supply of air is limited, the oxygen in the air may be used up before the fuel. The fuel is incompletely combusted.

If a hydrocarbon is **incompletely combusted**, the carbon in it may be:
* only partially oxidized, forming carbon monoxide
* unburnt, forming soot (as in a yellow Bunsen flame)

In car engines, turbos pump more air into the engine. This improves efficiency because it helps the fuel to combust completely.

Important ideas about chemical change 3: reactivity

DISPLACEMENT REACTIONS

Compare the reactivity of iron and copper by putting an iron nail into copper(II) sulphate solution and copper foil into iron(II) sulphate solution.

Iron nail — Blue solution → Iron nail — Green solution

Copper foil — Green solution → NO CHANGE

Observations
- the iron nail dissolves and gets smaller
- the solution changes from blue to green
- copper metal is deposited in the bottom of the beaker

Reaction
$Fe(s) + CuSO_4(aq) \rightarrow FeSO_4(aq) + Cu(s)$

or, because the sulphate ions do not take part and are only spectators:
$Fe(s) + Cu^{2+}(aq) \rightarrow Fe^{2+}(aq) + Cu(s)$

Observations
- no change

Reaction
None

Conclusion
These two experiments tell us that
- iron metal is more reactive than copper metal
- copper ions are more reactive than iron ions

Results from experiments like this show us some important ideas

---

- **The more reactive an element is, the less reactive are its compounds (and vice versa)**

METALS	METAL IONS IN SOLUTION	HALOGENS	HALIDE IONS IN SOLUTION
sodium	Na^+	fluorine	F^-
iron	Fe^{2+}	chlorine	Cl^-
copper	Cu^{2+}	bromine	Br^-
		iodine	I^-

REACTIVITY (with arrows indicating direction for each column)

- **Reactivity patterns in the main groups of the periodic table can be related to atomic structure**

Metal atoms react by losing electrons. Bigger atoms, further down the group hold their outer electrons less well, so are more reactive.

Non-metal atoms react by gaining electrons. Smaller atoms, near the top of the group attract electrons more, so react more.

There is no clear pattern of reactivity in the transition elements. A different table is needed.

- **A reactivity list for all metals gives us a guide for the reactivity of the transition elements as well**

- **The position of a metal in the reactivity list gives a guide to its uses and the method used to extract it.**

- **The detailed chemistry of the metal and its compounds is related to its position in the reactivity list, as the table on the next page shows.**

	Metal	Place in periodic table	Ion	
very reactive metals too reactive to be used	potassium	Group 1	K^+	**very unreactive ions** difficult to extract
	sodium	Group 1	Na^+	
	calcium	Group 2	Ca^{2+}	
less reactive metals many uses, especially aluminium, which is protected by an oxide layer	magnesium	Group 2	Mg^{2+}	
	aluminium	Group 3	Al^{3+}	
	zinc	transition element	Zn^{2+}	**more reactive ions** easier to extract
	iron	transition element	Fe^{2+}	
	lead	Group 4	Pb^{2+}	
unreactive metals many uses	copper	transition element	Cu^{2+}	**very reactive ions** metals found unreacted; used even by early humans
	silver	transition element	Ag^+	
	gold	transition element	Au^{2+}	

REACTIVITY

Metal reactivity and uses

METAL	REACTION WITH AIR	REACTION WITH WATER	REACTION WITH DILUTE ACID	EXTRACTION	USES	METAL
potassium		react quickly in cold water				potassium
sodium					**street lamps:** sodium and its compounds give orange light when heated	sodium
calcium	burn to form oxide		all these metals displace hydrogen from dilute acids; reactivity increases up the list	**electrolysis** of molten compound	**steel production:** calcium reacts with and removes oxygen	calcium
magnesium		burns in steam			**alloy with aluminium:** makes aluminium stronger **flares:** burns with a very bright light	magnesium
aluminium		oxide layer stops reaction			**major structural metal:** strong, but light; protected by oxide layer	aluminium
zinc		reacts in steam		reaction with carbon in **blast furnace**	**alloy with copper:** brass **sacrificial protection of steel:** galvanizing	zinc
iron		reacts reversibly in steam			**major structural metal:** cheap to extract and strong when alloyed with carbon, but it rusts	iron
hydrogen	react slowly when heated					hydrogen
copper		no reaction	metals below hydrogen never react with acids to displace hydrogen	decomposition by heat alone	**pipes:** ductile but unreactive **coinage:** colour, unreactive **electrical cables:** good conductor	copper
gold					**jewellery:** rare, attractive colour **electrical contacts:** good conductor, unreactive	gold

Notes
Hydrogen is in the list because many metal reactions involve the metal displacing hydrogen from water or acids.

Group 1 metals are kept under oil to stop reaction with air. Other metals form oxide layers which slow down further reaction.

The reactivity of aluminium appears *anomalous* or unexpected. It is a very reactive metal, but it appears to be unreactive because the oxide layer protects it.

Unreactive metals do not react to produce hydrogen. But some of them react with acids in other ways. For example, copper reacts with dilute nitric acid. In this reaction nitric acid is not acting as an acid (through the hydrogen ion) but as an oxidizing agent (through the nitrate ion).

The reactive metals have such unreactive compounds that they can only be decomposed by electrolysis.

The unreactive metals at the bottom of the list have such reactive compounds that the metals were discovered and used in prehistoric times.

Metal uses depend on a number of factors:
- **abundance of the metal:** aluminium is more abundant than iron; gold is very rare.
- **ease of extraction:** gold and iron are easy to extract; aluminium is expensive to extract because so much electricity is needed.
- **suitable physical and chemical properties:** these are listed above.

Water

BONDING AND STRUCTURE

slightly positive — slightly negative

Ḧ Ö Ḧ

slightly positive

The shared pairs in the covalent bonds are pulled nearer to the oxygen than the hydrogen.

This makes the hydrogen ends of the molecule a bit positive and the oxygen part a bit negative. This means the molecule is **polar**.

TESTS FOR WATER

Water can be recognized by
• its physical properties
It freezes at 0°C and boils at 100°C.
• its solvent properties
It dissolves anhydrous white copper sulphate turning it blue:

$$CuSO_4(s) \rightarrow CuSO_4.5H_2O(aq)$$
white blue

It dissolves anhydrous blue cobalt chloride turning it pink.

$$CoCl_2(s) \rightarrow CoCl_2.7H_2O(aq)$$
blue pink

SOLVENT PROPERTIES

The charged parts of each water molecule attract other molecules and ions making water a very good solvent.

Ionic solids (like salt) and **covalent solids** (like sugar) all get *more* soluble as the temperature increases.

Gases (like oxygen, carbon dioxide, and hydrogen chloride) get *less* soluble as the temperature increases. The oxygen dissolved in water is essential to aquatic life.

PURIFICATION

Because water is such a good solvent, it is difficult to find it pure. **Rainwater** contains dissolved gases. It dissolves gases like carbon dioxide (which occurs in the atmosphere naturally), and sulphur dioxide and nitrogen dioxide (which are in the atmosphere as a result of human activities).

PHYSICAL PROPERTIES

hydrogen bond

The charged parts of each molecule attract oppositely charged parts on nearby molecules strongly. These forces are called **hydrogen bonds**. They hold water molecules together tightly, so water is a liquid not a gas at room temperature.

AQUEOUS AMMONIA

AMMONIA IN SOLUTION

Ammonia gas is very soluble in water. It *takes a proton from water* (unlike the hydrogen halides which give a proton to water). The resulting solution is alkaline, because it contains hydroxide ions, OH⁻.

$$NH_3(g) + H_2O(l) \rightarrow NH_4^+(aq) + OH^-(aq)$$

HYDROGEN CHLORIDE IN SOLUTION

Hydrogen chloride and the other hydrogen halides are very soluble in water. They react with the water making *strongly acidic* solutions because they *give a proton to water* making the hydroxonium ion, H_3O^+. This is usually written more simply as H^+. So the reaction equation is

$$H_2O(l) + HCl(g) \rightarrow H_3O^+(aq) + Cl^-(aq)$$

$$\text{or} \quad HCl(g) \xrightarrow{H_2O} H^+(aq) + Cl^-(aq)$$

The resulting solution is called hydrochloric acid.

SALTS IN SOLUTION

Many ionic solids dissolve in water. Sea water is a source of these salts and the elements in them.

Sea water contains sodium chloride and small amounts of other metal halides. Bromine is extracted from the magnesium bromide in sea water by displacement with chlorine.

$$Cl_2(g) + MgBr_2(aq) \rightarrow MgCl_2(aq) + Br_2(aq)$$

SODA WATER

CARBON DIOXIDE IN SOLUTION

Carbon dioxide dissolves in water forming **carbonic acid**.

Rain is very dilute carbonic acid; soda water is a more concentrated solution.

$$H_2O(l) + CO_2(g) \rightarrow H_2CO_3(aq)$$

The water cycle

WATER AS A RESOURCE

Because water is cycled quickly it is a renewable resource. The time it spends in different parts of the cycle – the residence time – varies a lot. Water may be in the atmosphere for only a few hours; in a lake or river for days, weeks, or months; and in ice caps, glaciers, or oceans for thousands of years.

As water is cycled it dissolves
- gases like the oxides of carbon, nitrogen, and sulphur
- soluble solids from the ground it runs over or through.

These processes may be 'natural' (e.g. the formation of hard water) or 'unnatural' (e.g. dissolving pollutant gases to form acid rain).

Solar energy

Freezing
liquid → solid
(exothermic)

Condensation
gas → liquid
(exothermic)

Wind

Rain

Snow

Melting
solid → liquid
(endothermic)

Transpiration
liquid → gas
(endothermic)

Evaporation

Evaporation
liquid → gas
(endothermic)

Sea

Ground water in aquifers
(solution takes place)

Lakes and rivers

Toilets 33%
Washing and bathing 48%
Cleaning 10%
Cooking and drinking 1%

WATER TREATMENT PLANT

Storage tank

Reservoir water
Contains clay, algae, bacteria.

Aerator
Dissolved iron is oxidized forming a precipitate.

Mixing tank
Aluminium sulphate added to precipitate clay; chlorine added to kill bacteria.

Sedimentation tank
Clay particles settle out.

Filtration
Water filtered through beds of fine sand.

Chlorination tank
More chlorine added to kill all bacteria. Chlorine is a strong oxidizing agent and reacts with bacteria.

Water treatment plants cannot remove soluble impurities such as nitrates. So the water running off fields into rivers is monitored to check that leached nitrates stay below safe limits.

SEWAGE TREATMENT PLANT

To river

Methane

Slurry used to fertilize fields

Sedimenter

Sludge digester
Anaerobic bacteria contain enzymes which catalyse decomposition of harmful substances. Methane gas and fertilizer are produced.

Settling tanks
Solid particles sink to the bottom making sludge.

Aeration tank
Air is blown through water. Aerobic bacteria contain enzymes which catalyse the decomposition of harmful substances in the water.

The water cycle 27

Solubility and solutions in water

SOLUBILITY

The **solubility** of a substance is defined as the mass of that substance which will dissolve in 100 g of water at a defined temperature.

For most solids, the solubility **increases** with increasing temperature.

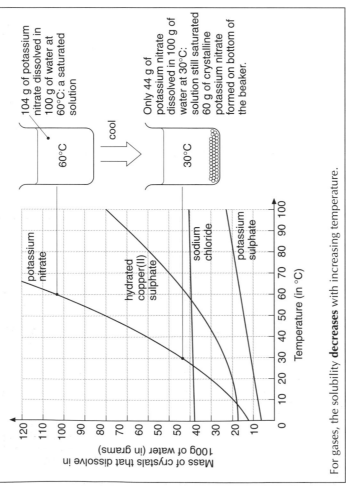

104 g of potassium nitrate dissolved in 100 g of water at 60°C: a saturated solution

60°C

cool

30°C

Only 44 g of potassium nitrate dissolved in 100 g of water at 30°C: solution still saturated 60 g of crystalline potassium nitrate formed on bottom of the beaker.

potassium nitrate

hydrated copper(II) sulphate

sodium chloride

potassium sulphate

Temperature (in °C)

Mass of crystals that dissolve in 100g of water (in grams)

For gases, the solubility **decreases** with increasing temperature.

SOAP, SCUM, AND DETERGENT

Soaps are the sodium salts of long carbon chain carboxylic acids.

In the presence of calcium (or magnesium) ions, a precipitation reaction takes place and the insoluble calcium (or magnesium) salt forms.

$$2 \, \text{\textasciitilde\textasciitilde\textasciitilde} \, C \overset{O}{\underset{O^-(aq)}{\diagdown}} + Ca^{2+}(aq) \rightarrow Ca^{2+} \left(\text{\textasciitilde\textasciitilde\textasciitilde} \, C \overset{O}{\underset{O}{\diagdown}} \right)_2 (s)$$

The calcium (and magnesium) salts of detergents are soluble, so detergents do not form scum with hard water.

HARD WATER

Water containing dissolved calcium or magnesium ions is said to be **hard**. In hard water soap does not lather as well and forms a scum. The calcium and magnesium ions get into the water in two ways.

1. Rain falls on soluble calcium or magnesium minerals and **dissolves** them.

2. Rain (which is slightly acidic) **reacts with** basic calcium or magnesium minerals. Rainwater is acidic because it contains dissolved carbon dioxide. So rain is dilute carbonic acid.

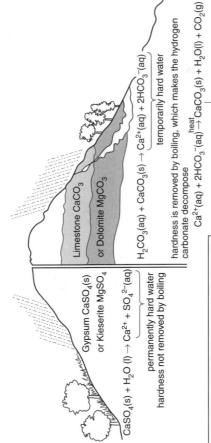

Gypsum $CaSO_4(s)$ or Kieserite $MgSO_4$

$CaSO_4(s) + H_2O(l) \rightarrow Ca^{2+} + SO_4^{2-}(aq)$
permanently hard water
hardness not removed by boiling

Limestone $CaCO_3$ or Dolomite $MgCO_3$

$H_2CO_3(aq) + CaCO_3(s) \rightarrow Ca^{2+}(aq) + 2HCO_3^-(aq)$
temporarily hard water

hardness is removed by boiling, which makes the hydrogen carbonate decompose
$Ca^{2+}(aq) + 2HCO_3^-(aq) \overset{heat}{\rightarrow} CaCO_3(s) + H_2O(l) + CO_2(g)$
'scale' in kettles and boilers

Advantages of hard water

- better taste
- healthier: less heart disease stronger bones and teeth
- better for brewing beer

Disadvantages of hard water

- forms a scum with soap
- forms a scale or 'fur' in hot water boilers and kettles

Softening water

Water which has had its hardness removed is described as softened water. Water is softened by:

1. Precipitating out the calcium or magnesium ions by adding sodium carbonate:
$$Ca^{2+}(aq) + CO_3^{2-}(aq) \rightarrow CaCO_3(s)$$

2. Ion exchange. The hard water is run through a resin which replaces the calcium or magnesium ions with sodium ions:
$$2Na\text{-resin} + Ca^{2+}(aq) \rightarrow Ca\text{-resin} + 2Na^+(aq)$$

Acids and bases

ACIDS

Acid properties

- sour taste: citric acid in lemons and grapefruits; ethanoic acid in vinegar (never taste acids in the lab)
- change the colour of indicators: litmus and universal indicators go red
- react with water to make hydrogen ions, H_3O^+, or more simply, $H^+(aq)$
  $$H_2O(l) + HNO_3(g) \rightarrow H^+(aq) + NO^{3-}(aq)$$
- react with reactive metals which displace the hydrogen in the acid
  $$Mg(s) + H_2SO_4(aq) \rightarrow MgSO_4(aq) + H_2(g)$$
- react with metal oxides, metal hydroxides, and metal carbonates to make salts; when this happens the acid is *neutralized*.

Strong and weak acids

Some acids react completely with water forming hydrogen ions:

$$H_2O(l) + HCl(g) \rightarrow H^+(aq) + Cl^-(aq)$$

The solution made conducts strongly because it contains so many ions. These acids are called strong acids.

Other acids react incompletely with water, and only make a few hydrogen ions:

$$H_2O(l) + CH_3COOH(l) \rightleftharpoons H^+(aq) + CH_3COO^-(aq)$$
$$99.9\% \qquad\qquad 0.1\% \qquad 0.1\%$$

Because there are so few ions present in the solution, it conducts weakly. Acids like this are called weak acids.

So
- **strong acids are fully ionized** in water
- **weak acids are only partially ionized** in water.

Definition of an acid

An acid is a substance which contains hydrogen which can be displaced by a metal and which reacts with water to make hydrogen ions as the only positive ions.

Bee stings are acidic – treat with sodium hydrogencarbonate.

Common acids

Strong

hydrochloric	HCl
nitric	HNO_3
sulphuric	H_2SO_4

Weak

carbonic	H_2CO_3
ethanoic	CH_3COOH
sulphurous	H_2SO_3

BASES

Bases and alkalis

Substances which neutralize acids are called **bases**.

Bases are the oxides, hydroxides, or carbonates of metals.

Most bases are insoluble, but some dissolve in water.

Soluble bases are called **alkalis**.

Strong and weak alkalis

Some alkalis split up completely into ions:
$$NaOH(s) + H_2O(l) \rightarrow$$
$$Na^+(aq) + OH^-(aq)$$

They are called strong alkalis.

Other alkalis react incompletely with water making only a few hydroxide ions:
$$NH_3(aq) + H_2O(l) \rightleftharpoons$$
$$NH_4^+(aq) + OH^-(aq)$$

They are called weak alkalis.

Common alkalis

Group 1 oxides, hydroxides, and carbonates: NaOH; K_2O; Na_2CO_3

Calcium hydroxide (lime water): $Ca(OH)_2$

Ammonia solution (aqueous ammonia): $NH_3(aq)$

Wasp stings are alkaline – treat with lemon juice or vinegar.

Alkaline solutions

The solution made from a soluble base:
- has a soapy, slippery feel – most soaps are alkaline
- changes the colour of indicators – litmus and universal go blue.

Neutralization

pH
The acidity or alkalinity of a solution can be measured on the pH scale, which goes from 0 to 14.

ACIDIC													ALKALINE	

pH	0	1	2	3	4	5	6	7	8	9	10	11	12	13	14

strong acids HCl   *weak acids* H_2CO_3 *neutral solutions* NaCl   *weak bases* NH_3 *strong bases* NaOH

e.g.

litmus colour   red   purple   blue

Acidic solutions have pH values less than 7.

Neutral solutions have pH values of 7 at room temperature.

Alkaline or basic solutions have pH values greater than 7.

NEUTRALIZATION
When an acid and a base react together they **neutralize** each other. The acid loses its acidic properties and the base loses its basic properties. The products of a neutralization reaction are a salt and water.

acid + base → salt + water (+ carbon dioxide if the base is a carbonate)

e.g. $NaOH + HCl → NaCl + H_2O$
$MgO + H_2SO_4 → MgSO_4 + H_2O$
$CaCO_3 + 2HNO_3 → Ca(NO_3)_2 + H_2O + CO_2$

During these reactions:
- the hydrogen ions from the acid react with the hydroxide ions from the base to make water molecules

  $H^+(aq) + OH^-(aq) → H_2O(l)$

- all the other ions are spectators and just stay in solution

- heat is produced because all neutralizations are exothermic

- the pH changes

- the colour of an indicator changes.

USING NEUTRALIZATIONS
There are a number of important examples of neutralization.

1. Adding lime (calcium hydroxide) to soil
Plants need nitrogen, phosphorus, and potassium compounds from the soil to grow well. Most plants take up these elements better when the soil is alkaline. Lime neutralizes acids in the soil making it alkaline.

2. Reducing acid rain and its effects
The coal burnt in power stations contains sulphur as an impurity. When the coal is burnt, the sulphur is burnt too. This produces sulphur dioxide, which dissolves in rain forming acid rain. By passing the burnt gases through lime, they are neutralized. The product, calcium sulphate, is used as plaster.

Many lakes have become acidic due to acid rain. All the fish in them die. Spraying powdered lime on to the lake neutralizes the water so that fish can once again survive.

3. Neutralizing stomach acids
The human stomach contains hydrochloric acid so that the enzyme pepsin can begin digesting protein. Sometimes too much acid is made and begins to attack the stomach wall causing pain. The extra acid can be neutralized by taking an 'ant-acid'. These always contain a base such as sodium or magnesium carbonate.

ACIDS WITH TWO HYDROGENS
Some acids like sulphuric, H_2SO_4, and carbonic, H_2CO_3, have two hydrogens in them. These acids can be

- **completely neutralized** when both hydrogens are replaced, e.g.
  $H_2CO_3 + 2NaOH → Na_2CO_3 + 2H_2O$
  complete neutralization

- or **partly neutralized** when only one hydrogen is replaced, e.g.
  $H_2CO_3 + 1NaOH → NaHCO_3 + 1H_2O$
  partial neutralization

The salt made by partial neutralization is called an **acid salt**. In this example the salt is called **sodium hydrogencarbonate**.

SALTS
Salts are substances in which the hydrogen of an acid has been replaced by a metal, e.g. NaCl or $MgSO_4$.

Each acid can produce a family of salts.

e.g.
hydrochloric acid produces **chlorides**
nitric acid produces **nitrates**
sulphuric acid produces **sulphates**
ethanoic acid produces **ethanoates**

The first part of the salt, the metal part, is determined by the base used to react with the acid. So each base also produces a family of salts.

e.g.
sodium bases like sodium hydroxide produce **sodium salts**
magnesium bases like magnesium oxide produce **magnesium salts**

Crystallization and precipitation

CRYSTALLIZATION

If the water in a solution is lost by evaporation, the ions that are left will clump together. The positive cations will attract the negative anions, and the ions will arrange themselves so that oppositely charged ions are next to each other. A lattice will slowly form. This process is called **crystallization**.

e.g. $Na^+(aq) + Cl^-(aq) \rightarrow NaCl(s)$

If the process happens slowly, big crystals have time to grow.
If the process happens quickly, lots of small crystals form.

SLOW

Warm, saturated solution

Cold, saturated solution

PRECIPITATION

If two solutions containing oppositely charged ions which attract each other very strongly are added together, the ions will immediately clump together. Because this happens very quickly, there is not time for an ordered lattice to form. So instead of crystals, a fine suspension is seen. This is called a **precipitate**.

Precipitation is the reaction between two solutions making an *insoluble* product.

e.g.

$CaCl_2(aq) + Na_2CO_3(aq) \rightarrow CaCO_3(s) + 2NaCl(aq)$

or much better

$Ca^{2+}(aq) + CO_3^{2-}(aq) \rightarrow CaCO_3(s)$

because the other ions are spectators.

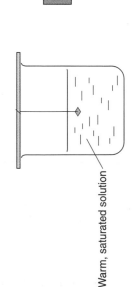

FAST

Transparent solutions

Opaque suspension

Using precipitation reactions
1. Making insoluble salts

Any insoluble salt can be made simply by adding together two solutions containing between them the ions in the salt.

So to make lead iodide, add any lead solution to any iodide solution, filter off and wash the precipitate, then dry it.

2. Testing for the presence of certain ions

Precipitation reactions can be used to test for both anions and cations.

Anion tests

Anions like the halides and sulphates can be tested for using precipitation reactions. For example, the presence of chloride ions in solution can be detected by adding silver ions. Silver ions attract chloride ions so strongly that if there are any chloride ions present a white precipitate of silver chloride will form.

(Equally, silver ions can be tested for using chloride ions.)

A systematic scheme for testing for anions is shown on page 67.

Cation tests

Many metals form insoluble hydroxides. So if a solution of sodium hydroxide is added to a solution of the metal, a precipitate of the hydroxide will be seen. Hydroxide precipitates vary in colour, and some redissolve when excess sodium hydroxide is added.

A systematic scheme for testing for cations is shown on page 66.

Reduction and oxidation

REDUCTION

Reduction is the removal of oxygen. The word was originally used to describe the process of changing a metal ore (often an oxide) into the metal.

e.g. $2CuO(s) + C(s) \rightarrow 2Cu(s) + CO_2(g)$

The metal oxide above would not have been reduced without the carbon, so the carbon is called a **reducing agent**.

Notice that in acting as a reducing agent, the carbon is itself oxidized. This means that the copper oxide was acting as an **oxidizing agent**.

Ore   Pure metal

OXIDATION

Oxidation is the reaction of an element or compound with oxygen.

e.g. $2Mg(s) + O_2(g) \rightarrow 2MgO(s)$
or $CH_4(g) + 2O_2(g) \rightarrow CO_2(g) + 2H_2O(g)$

Magnesium being oxidized

Oxidizing agents

Oxidizing agents are substances that oxidize the substances they react with. They themselves are easily *reduced*.

Common oxidizing agents are: oxygen, the halogens, potassium dichromate(VI), potassium manganate(VII).

OXIDIZING AGENT
causes oxidation

is reduced

is oxidized

REDUCING AGENT
causes reduction

Reducing agents

Reducing agents are substances that reduce the substances they react with. They themselves are easily *oxidized*.

Common reducing agents are: reactive metals; carbon; carbon monoxide

REDOX

Reduction and oxidation take place together. All oxidation reactions involve the reduction of something else, so whether the process is called oxidation or reduction depends on which reactant is being referred to. So the whole process is often called **redox**.

Electron transfer

Magnesium atoms and oxygen molecules react to form magnesium oxide, an ionic solid. In this solid there are magnesium ions, Mg^{2+}, and oxide ions, O^{2-}.

So the magnesium (which is oxidized) loses electrons as the atoms become positive cations:
$Mg \rightarrow Mg^{2+} + 2e^-$

while the oxygen (which is reduced) gains electrons as the molecules become negative anions:
$O_2 + 4e^- \rightarrow 2O^{2-}$

So, oxidation and reduction can also be defined in terms of electron loss and gain.

Oxidation is loss of electrons. **Reduction** is gain of electrons. **Redox** is electron transfer.

Remember **OIL RIG**! **O**xidation **I**s **L**oss, **R**eduction **I**s **G**ain.

ELECTROLYSIS

Electrolytic reactions are examples of redox reactions.

Anode reactions are **oxidations**.

At the positive anode, electrons are lost from anions:

e.g. $2Cl^- \rightarrow Cl_2 + 2e^-$
or $2O^{2-} \rightarrow O_2 + 4e^-$

Cathode reactions are **reductions**.
At the negative cathode, electrons are gained by cations:

e.g. $Na^+ + e^- \rightarrow Na$
and $Al^{3+} + 3e^- \rightarrow Al$

DISPLACEMENT REACTIONS

Displacement reactions are also redox reactions. For example:

A more reactive metal is oxidized, while a less reactive one is reduced.

$Fe + Cu^{2+} \rightarrow Fe^{2+} + Cu$

A more reactive non-metal is reduced while a less reactive one is oxidized:

$Cl_2 + 2I^- \rightarrow 2Cl^- + I_2$

Reversible reactions

In some reactions the products can react themselves, making the original reactants. In other words, the reaction can go both ways. It is **reversible**. This is shown in a written equation using the **equilibrium sign** ⇌.

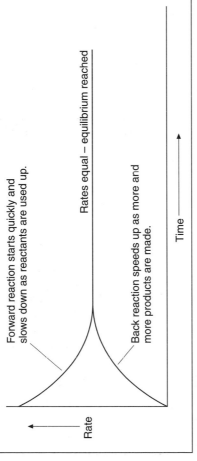

forward reaction

reactants ⇌ products

back reaction

The reaction from left to right is called the **forward reaction**.

The reaction from right to left is called the **back reaction**.

The substances on the *left* of the equation are called **reactants** and those on the *right* are called **products**, whichever reaction (forward or back) is being referred to.

EQUILIBRIUM SYSTEMS

To begin with, reactants react making products. As the reactants get used up, the forward reaction slows down. As more and more product is made, the back reaction speeds up. Eventually the two rates are equal. Reactants are making products as quickly as products are making reactants. The system is said to be in **dynamic equilibrium**. Although reactions are going on, no visible change is seen because the two reactions in opposite directions cancel each other out.

Rate

Forward reaction starts quickly and slows down as reactants are used up.

Rates equal – equilibrium reached

Back reaction speeds up as more and more products are made.

Time

CHANGING CONDITIONS IN EQUILIBRIUM SYSTEMS

An equilibrium system does not appear to change from the outside, but inside both forward and back reactions are happening.

When the temperature or pressure changes, or when the amount of one of the reactants or products changes, the two rates change. They change by different amounts, so they no longer cancel each other out. *For a time* one reaction is faster than the other. The system is not at equilibrium, so changes can be detected as reactants are made faster than products, or products are made faster than reactants. Eventually, the system reaches a new equilibrium position, which is different from the first.

Le Chatelier's principle

The way an equilibrium system reacts when the conditions are changed can be predicted using a general rule called le **Chatelier's principle**.

This states that *when a change is applied to an equilibrium system, the system will alter in such a way as to oppose the change.*

Using the Haber process for making ammonia as an example, we can see how this rule works:

The reaction for the Haber process is:
$N_2(g) + 3H_2(g) \rightleftharpoons 2NH_3(g) + heat$
(the reaction is exothermic)

Increasing the pressure

If the pressure is increased, the equilibrium system reacts to reduce the pressure. It does this by moving to the right because there are only 2 molecules on the right of the equation, but four on the left.

MORE MOLES   SQUEEZE   FEWER MOLES

$N_2(g) + 3H_2(g) \rightleftharpoons 2NH_3(g) + heat$

So an increase in pressure increases the yield of ammonia for a given amount of reactants.

Increasing the temperature

If the temperature is increased, the equilibrium system reacts to remove heat. It does this by moving in the endothermic direction. For an exothermic reaction like the Haber process, this means moving to the left. So increasing the temperature of the Haber process decreases the yield of ammonia.

For a system where the forward reaction is endothermic, increasing the temperature increases the yield of product.

FORWARD REACTION IS EXOTHERMIC

Energy

Products

Reactants

Heating favours reactants in exothermic reactions. In the Haber process, heating means less ammonia is made.

FORWARD REACTION IS ENDOTHERMIC

Energy

Products

Reactants

Heating favours products in endothermic reactions.

Measuring rates of reaction

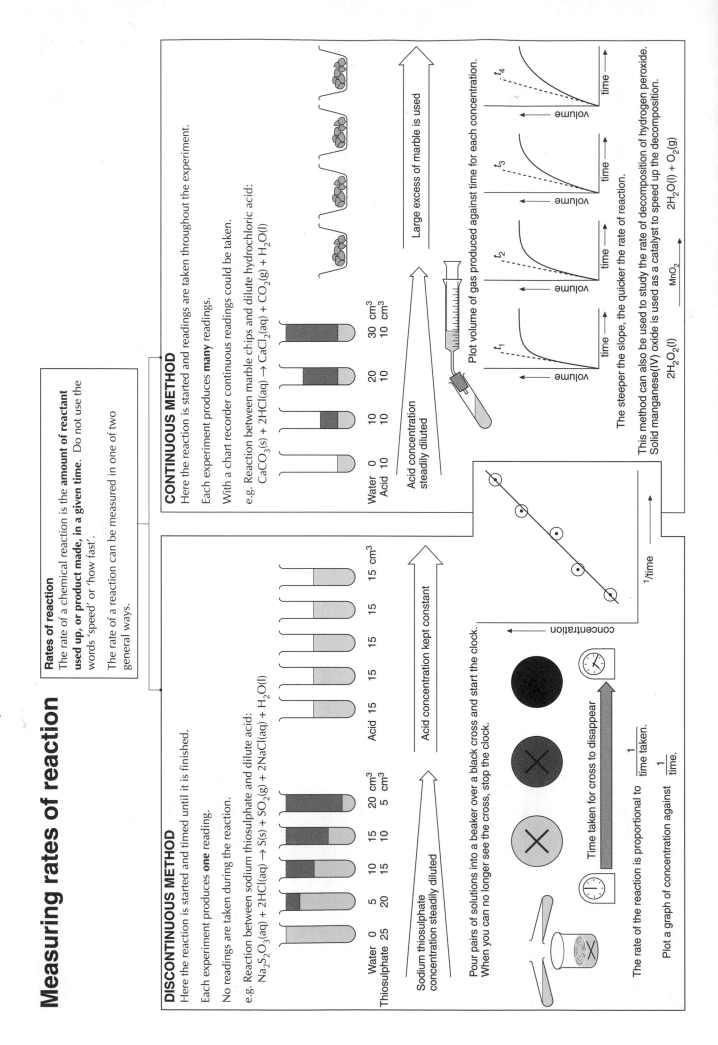

Rates of reaction

The rate of a chemical reaction is the **amount of reactant used up, or product made, in a given time**. Do not use the words 'speed' or 'how fast'.

The rate of a reaction can be measured in one of two general ways.

DISCONTINUOUS METHOD

Here the reaction is started and timed until it is finished.

Each experiment produces **one** reading.

No readings are taken during the reaction.

e.g. Reaction between sodium thiosulphate and dilute acid:
$Na_2S_2O_3(aq) + 2HCl(aq) \rightarrow S(s) + SO_2(g) + 2NaCl(aq) + H_2O(l)$

| Water | 0 | 5 | 10 | 15 | 20 cm³ |
| Thiosulphate | 25 | 20 | 15 | 10 | 5 cm³ |

Sodium thiosulphate concentration steadily diluted

| Acid | 15 | 15 | 15 | 15 | 15 cm³ |

Acid concentration kept constant

Pour pairs of solutions into a beaker over a black cross and start the clock. When you can no longer see the cross, stop the clock.

Time taken for cross to disappear

The rate of the reaction is proportional to $\dfrac{1}{\text{time taken}}$.

Plot a graph of concentration against $\dfrac{1}{\text{time}}$.

concentration

¹/time

CONTINUOUS METHOD

Here the reaction is started and readings are taken throughout the experiment.

Each experiment produces **many** readings.

With a chart recorder continuous readings could be taken.

e.g. Reaction between marble chips and dilute hydrochloric acid:
$CaCO_3(s) + 2HCl(aq) \rightarrow CaCl_2(aq) + CO_2(g) + H_2O(l)$

| Water | 0 | 10 | 20 | 30 cm³ |
| Acid | 10 | 10 | 10 | 10 cm³ |

Acid concentration steadily diluted

Large excess of marble is used

Plot volume of gas produced against time for each concentration.

t_1 t_2 t_3 t_4

volume / time

The steeper the slope, the quicker the rate of reaction.

This method can also be used to study the rate of decomposition of hydrogen peroxide. Solid manganese(IV) oxide is used as a catalyst to speed up the decomposition.

$2H_2O_2(l) \xrightarrow{MnO_2} 2H_2O(l) + O_2(g)$

Factors affecting reaction rates

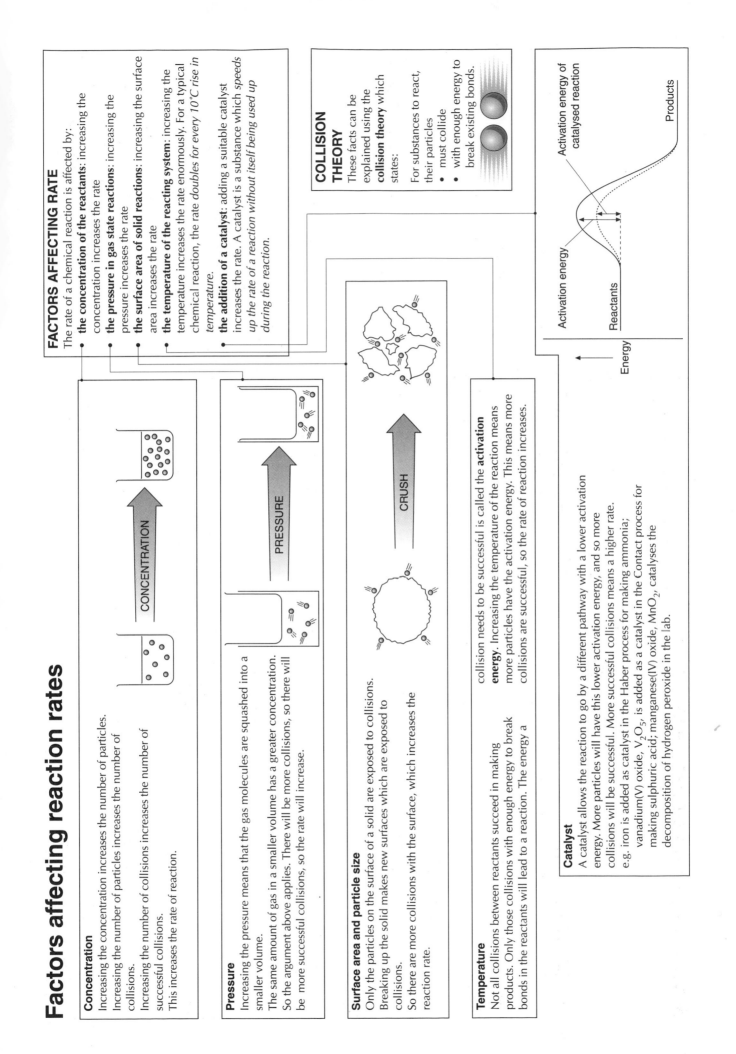

FACTORS AFFECTING RATE

The rate of a chemical reaction is affected by:

- **the concentration of the reactants**: increasing the concentration increases the rate
- **the pressure in gas state reactions**: increasing the pressure increases the rate
- **the surface area of solid reactions**: increasing the surface area increases the rate
- **the temperature of the reacting system**: increasing the temperature increases the rate enormously. For a typical chemical reaction, the rate *doubles for every 10°C rise in temperature.*
- **the addition of a catalyst**: adding a suitable catalyst increases the rate. A catalyst is a substance which *speeds up the rate of a reaction without itself being used up during the reaction.*

COLLISION THEORY

These facts can be explained using the **collision theory** which states:

For substances to react, their particles
- must collide
- with enough energy to break existing bonds.

Activation energy of catalysed reaction

Activation energy

Reactants

Products

Energy

Concentration

Increasing the concentration increases the number of particles.
Increasing the number of particles increases the number of collisions.
Increasing the number of collisions increases the number of successful collisions.
This increases the rate of reaction.

CONCENTRATION

Pressure

Increasing the pressure means that the gas molecules are squashed into a smaller volume.
The same amount of gas in a smaller volume has a greater concentration.
So the argument above applies. There will be more collisions, so there will be more successful collisions, so the rate will increase.

PRESSURE

Surface area and particle size

Only the particles on the surface of a solid are exposed to collisions.
Breaking up the solid makes new surfaces which are exposed to collisions.
So there are more collisions with the surface, which increases the reaction rate.

CRUSH

Temperature

Not all collisions between reactants succeed in making products. Only those collisions with enough energy to break bonds in the reactants will lead to a reaction. The energy a collision needs to be successful is called the **activation energy**. Increasing the temperature of the reaction means more particles have the activation energy. This means more collisions are successful, so the rate of reaction increases.

Catalyst

A catalyst allows the reaction to go by a different pathway with a lower activation energy. More particles will have this lower activation energy, and so more collisions will be successful. More successful collisions means a higher rate. e.g. iron is added as catalyst in the Haber process for making ammonia; vanadium(V) oxide, V_2O_5, is added as a catalyst in the Contact process for making sulphuric acid; manganese(IV) oxide, MnO_2, catalyses the decomposition of hydrogen peroxide in the lab.

Reactions involving enzymes

Enzyme structure

Enzymes are covalent macromolecules made of amino acids bonded together making a protein. The amino acid chains are folded and twisted forming globular proteins with specific reactive sites.

Reactive site

Enzyme catalysis

Enzymes catalyse specific reactions in living cells by providing a reaction pathway with a lower activation energy.

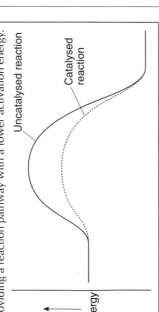

Uncatalysed reaction

Catalysed reaction

Energy

pH dependence

The shape of an enzyme depends on the hydrogen bonds between different parts of the amino acid chain, and hydrogen bonds are affected by pH. So each enzyme works best at a particular pH.

Pepsin in the stomach works best in acid conditions.

Trypsin in the lower gut works best in alkaline conditions.

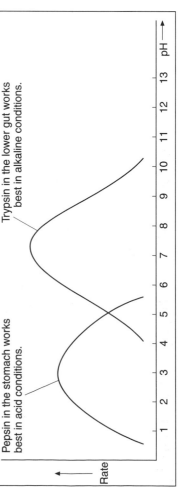

Rate

pH

ENZYMES

- are all proteins found in living cells
- catalyse reactions in cells
- can each catalyse only one specific reaction
- act within a narrow pH range
- act within a narrow temperature range

Temperature dependence

At this temperature the protein molecule begins to lose its shape. It is denatured.

Rate increases with temperature because there are more successful collisions.

The reactants no longer fit the reactive site. Catalysis stops. This is irreversible. Cooling will not restore the catalytic activity of the enzyme.

Rate

Temperature (in °C)

Enzyme lock and key mechanism

Reactant molecules fit into the reactive site of an enzyme like a key into a lock. Each reactive site only fits a particular reactant, so each enzyme catalyses only one reaction. Once in the site, the reactants react more quickly to form products.

Enzyme   Reactant

Products

Enzyme

USES OF ENZYMES

Digestion

Digestive enzymes convert insoluble substances in food into soluble substances which the body can absorb. They do this by breaking certain bonds one after another. Each bond is broken by a particular enzyme, and each enzyme needs particular conditions. This is why the pH changes through the gut.

Fermentation and baking

Fermentation is the anaerobic decomposition of simple carbohydrates into alcohol and carbon dioxide:

$$C_6H_{12}O_6 \rightarrow 2CO_2 + 2CH_3CH_2OH$$

This reaction is used in the brewing and wine making industries to make alcoholic drinks. In the baking industry the carbon dioxide produced makes the dough rise.

Yoghurt

Milk at 40°C is inoculated with bacteria. Enzymes in the bacteria convert the lactose in milk to lactic acid, which makes the milk thicken and curdle.

Detergents

Enzymes are added to detergents to help digest protein stains. Dirty washing is soaked in tepid water with a pH between 4 and 8, before being washed normally in hot water.

The enzymes used in detergents can sometimes cause allergic reactions such as asthma.

Formation of Earth's atmosphere

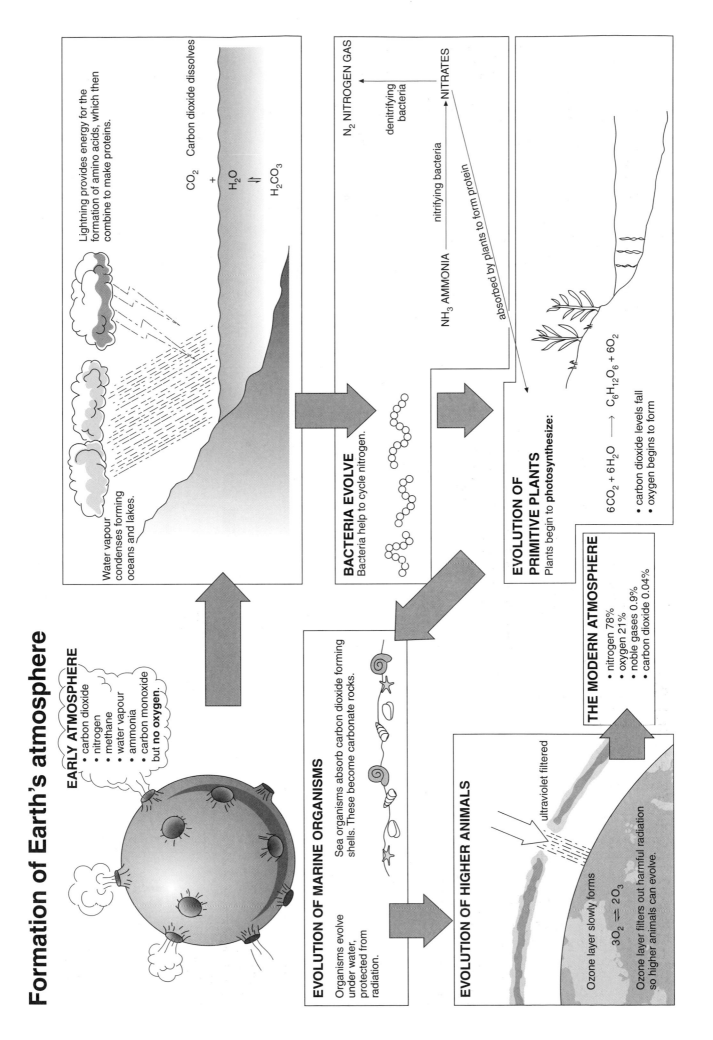

EARLY ATMOSPHERE
- carbon dioxide
- nitrogen
- methane
- water vapour
- ammonia
- carbon monoxide
but **no oxygen**.

Lightning provides energy for the formation of amino acids, which then combine to make proteins.

Water vapour condenses forming oceans and lakes.

CO_2 Carbon dioxide dissolves

$CO_2 + H_2O \rightleftharpoons H_2CO_3$

EVOLUTION OF MARINE ORGANISMS

Organisms evolve under water, protected from radiation.

Sea organisms absorb carbon dioxide forming shells. These become carbonate rocks.

BACTERIA EVOLVE
Bacteria help to cycle nitrogen.

N_2 NITROGEN GAS

denitrifying bacteria

NITRATES

NH_3 AMMONIA   nitrifying bacteria

absorbed by plants to form protein

EVOLUTION OF PRIMITIVE PLANTS
Plants begin to **photosynthesize**:

$6CO_2 + 6H_2O \longrightarrow C_6H_{12}O_6 + 6O_2$

- carbon dioxide levels fall
- oxygen begins to form

EVOLUTION OF HIGHER ANIMALS

ultraviolet filtered

Ozone layer slowly forms

$3O_2 \rightleftharpoons 2O_3$

Ozone layer filters out harmful radiation so higher animals can evolve.

THE MODERN ATMOSPHERE
- nitrogen 78%
- oxygen 21%
- noble gases 0.9%
- carbon dioxide 0.04%

Changes in the atmosphere

CARBON DIOXIDE AND THE GREENHOUSE EFFECT

$H_2O + CO_2 \rightarrow H_2CO_3$

dilute carbonic acid

solution

photosynthesis

$6CO_2 + 6H_2O \rightarrow C_6H_{12}O_6 + 6O_2$

respiration

$C_6H_{12}O_6 + 6O_2 \rightarrow 6CO_2 + 6H_2O$

burning of fuels

The burning of fossil fuels and the cutting down of trees contribute to an increase in atmospheric carbon dioxide.

Most solar radiation is reflected back from Earth but …

… carbon dioxide absorbs infrared radiation. This gives Earth its warm atmosphere, which makes life possible. This is called the greenhouse effect.

The increase in carbon dioxide in the atmosphere (top graph) has been accompanied by a rise in temperature of the atmosphere (bottom graph). Many scientists think these are linked. They call this the **enhanced greenhouse effect** or **global warming**.

CO₂ concentration (parts per million)

350
340
330
320
310
300
290
280

1850 1870 1890 1910 1930 1950 1970 1990

The increase in carbon dioxide since 1850

Temperature deviation from 1850-1980 mean

0.6
0.4
0.2
0
-0.2
-0.4
-0.6
-0.8

1850 1870 1890 1910 1930 1950 1970 1990

The rise in temperature since 1850

OZONE LAYER

The layer of ozone gas high in the atmosphere absorbs damaging high-energy radiation. The amount of ozone in the ozone layer is decreasing. This is caused by a number of gases, but especially chlorofluorocarbons (CFCs), which react with ozone. CFCs have been used in aerosols as propellants and in fridges as coolants. Thinning of the ozone layer leads to more skin cancer, cataracts, and damage to plants.

CFCs

old fridge

CFCs are being replaced with **hydrofluoroalkanes** (HFAs) which are more strongly bonded and do not react with ozone.

ACID RAIN

Coal used in power stations contains sulphur, so **sulphur dioxide** forms when the coal is burnt. Sulphur dioxide dissolves in rain to form sulphuric acid.

Exhaust from vehicles contains **oxides of nitrogen**. These react with rain making nitric acid.

Acid rain kills trees and fish. Lime is added to lakes to neutralize the acid.

15th January 1985
8am-6pm

■ pH of 4.6 and below

East wind

Areas of acid rain show that most of it is centred on industrial regions of the country. But pollutants in the atmosphere can move as the air moves, so other places are also affected.

Products from air

FIXATION OF NITROGEN AND THE HABER PROCESS

- Plants are made of cells – cells have nuclei – nuclei contain proteins – proteins are made from amino acids – amino acids contain nitrogen.
- **Fixation** is the conversion of unreactive atmospheric nitrogen into reactive compounds that plants can absorb.

NATURAL FIXATION

- thunderstorms

- bacterial nodules on roots of leguminous plants

Increasing demand for crops from a growing world population means these natural processes are no longer enough. **Fertilizers** are used to return nitrogen and other elements to the soil. The elements in fertilizers which plants need are **nitrogen**, **phosphorus**, and **potassium** (N,P,K).

FRACTIONAL DISTILLATION OF AIR

Air is a mixture so is separated by a physical process.

Because b.p.s are close together, **fractional distillation** is used.

Nitrogen b.p. −196°C
Used for:
- shrink fitting
- keeping flammable materials safe
- food freezing
- food packaging

Argon b.p. −186°C
Used for:
- arc welding
- light bulbs

Oxygen b.p. −183°C
Used for:
- steel making
- aerating rivers
- oxyacetylene cutting
- medical uses

Dried, filtered air

SYNTHETIC FIXATION – THE HABER PROCESS

Nitrogen is fixed synthetically by combining it with hydrogen to make ammonia, NH_3.

Raw materials
- water
- natural gas – source of hydrogen
- air – source of nitrogen

Reactions

$$CH_4 + H_2O \rightarrow CO + 3H_2$$
$$2CO + O_2 \rightarrow 2CO_2$$
air
$$N_2 \rightarrow$$

HABER PROCESS

$$3H_2(g) + N_2(g) \rightleftharpoons 2NH_3(g) + heat$$

Conditions
- Temperature: 300–500°C
- Pressure: 200–1000 atmospheres
- Catalyst: lumps of iron metal

Yield
About 15% conversion. Unreacted gases are recycled.

AMMONIA IS OXIDIZED TO NITRIC ACID

$$4NH_3(g) + 5O_2(g) \rightleftharpoons 4NO(g) + 6H_2O(g)$$
$$2NO(g) + O_2(g) \rightleftharpoons 2NO_2(g)$$
$$4NO_2(g) + O_2(g) + 2H_2O(l) \rightarrow 4HNO_3(l)$$

AMMONIA IS NEUTRALIZED

Some ammonia is used directly as fertilizer, but most fertilizers are ammonium salts.

$$NH_3(aq) + HNO_3(aq) \rightarrow NH_4NO_3(s)$$
$$2NH_3(aq) + H_2SO_4(aq) \rightarrow (NH_4)_2SO_4(s)$$

LEACHING OF FERTILIZERS

Fertilizers have to be soluble to be absorbed by plants.

Rain falling on fertilized ground dissolves the fertilizer and washes it from the soil into rivers and lakes. This is called **leaching.**

The leaching of fertilizers has two bad effects:

1. **Nitrates get into drinking water.** This is bad for health. A condition in young babies called blue baby syndrome has been linked to nitrate levels in drinking water.

2. The leached fertilizer causes excessive growth of algae and other water plants. Bacteria use up all the oxygen in the rivers or lakes as they digest plant matter, and the river or lake water becomes black and foul smelling. This is called **eutrophication.**

Choosing conditions for the Haber process

REACTION

$$N_2(g) + 3H_2(g) \rightleftharpoons 2NH_3(g) + \text{heat}$$

:N≡N:

quite a strong bond
436 kJ mol⁻¹ → 436 kJ mol^{-1}

very strongly bonded
944 kJ mol⁻¹ → 944 kJ mol^{-1}

weaker bonds than in the reactants
388 kJ mol⁻¹ → 388 kJ mol^{-1}

The reactant molecules (N_2 and H_2) are very strongly bonded. Only collisions with a huge amount of energy will be successful, because the activation energy is very high. This means that the rate of the forward reaction making ammonia will be very slow unless the temperature is high. But if the temperature is high, the relatively weak bonds in ammonia will break and the back reaction will speed up. So a high temperature is needed to supply the activation energy, but a high temperature makes the product decompose more quickly.

THE PROBLEM

The best yield of ammonia will be produced under high pressure and low temperature. *(implied)*

LE CHATELIER

Le Chatelier's principle predicts that the best yield of ammonia will be produced under high pressure and low temperature.

Pressure

There are more moles of reactants than products, so high pressure favours products.

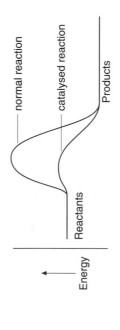

4 moles of reactants

squeeze

2 moles of products

Temperature

The reaction is exothermic (it produces heat), so cooling it will favour the forward reaction.

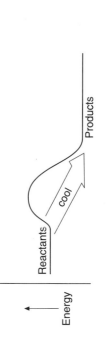

SOLVING THE PROBLEM

The actual conditions used in industry

1. Catalyst

Adding an iron catalyst lowers the activation energy, so a lower temperature can be used.

normal reaction

catalysed reaction

2. Pressure

Between 200 and 1000 atmospheres pressure are used. The higher the pressure the greater the yield but the costlier the plant. Most operate at around 500 atmospheres.

3. Temperature

A temperature between 300 and 500°C is used. This reduces the yield to about 15%, but increases the rate. The unreacted nitrogen and hydrogen gases are recycled.

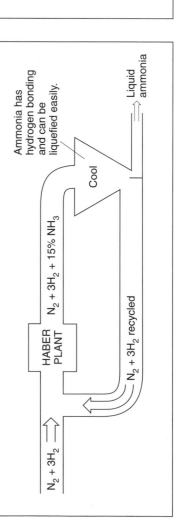

$N_2 + 3H_2$

HABER PLANT

$N_2 + 3H_2 + 15\% NH_3$

$N_2 + 3H_2$ recycled

Cool

Ammonia has hydrogen bonding and can be liquefied easily.

Liquid ammonia

Natural cycles

Natural cycles are very important because:
1. They maintain various elements so that they can be used again and again.
2. They maintain a balance or equilibrium in different parts of the cycle by replacing an element as it is used up.

When these cycles are disturbed by human activities, environmental problems build up. Either a resource runs out, or some substance builds up in concentration and causes pollution.

NITROGEN CYCLE

CARBON CYCLE

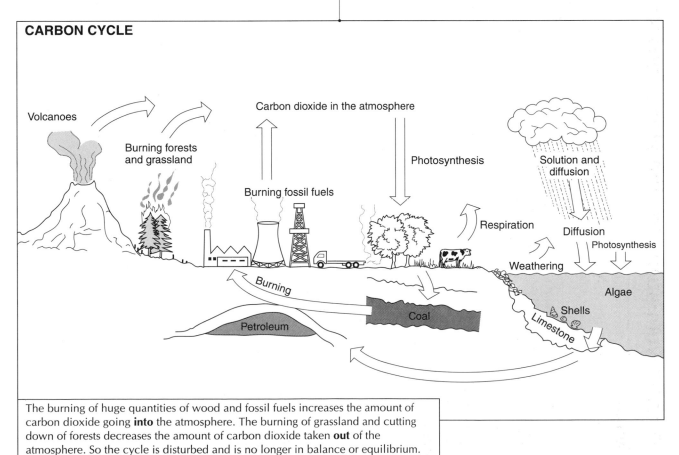

The burning of huge quantities of wood and fossil fuels increases the amount of carbon dioxide going **into** the atmosphere. The burning of grassland and cutting down of forests decreases the amount of carbon dioxide taken **out** of the atmosphere. So the cycle is disturbed and is no longer in balance or equilibrium. The result is **global warming** (the enhanced greenhouse effect), see p. 38.

The rock cycle and different kinds of rocks

SEDIMENTARY ROCKS

Sedimentary rocks are rocks formed by **deposition**.
They are formed by the following steps:
1. **weathering**: the breaking down of an existing rock
2. **transport and erosion**
3. **deposition**
4. **lithification**

Different kinds of sedimentary rock
- **clastic**: made from pieces of older rock
  e.g. mudstone, sandstone, conglomerate
- **chemical**: made by precipitation from suspension
  e.g. limestone, dolomite
- **evaporites**: made by crystallization from solution
  e.g. rock salt, gypsum
- **biological**: made from plant remains
  e.g. coal

Important features
- layers or strata
- rounded grains in clastic ones
- fossils

Deposition in layers or strata
Lower layers are older.

SEDIMENTS

Lithification
Pressure and cementation harden the sediments.

Getting older

Weathering
Physical: heating and cooling
causes exfoliation
freezing and thawing
causes cracking
Chemical: reaction with rain water
Biological: burrowing animals
tree roots
mining

Transport and erosion
By wind and water. Rock
particles become smaller
and rounder.

Folding and uplift

Glacier

Folding and uplift

METAMORPHIC

SEDIMENTARY ROCKS

METAMORPHIC ROCKS

Metamorphic rocks are rocks which have been changed by
the effects of
1. **high pressure**
2. **high temperature**

Both igneous and sedimentary rocks can become
metamorphic.
e.g. limestone is changed into marble
mudstone or shale into slate

Under conditions of high pressure and temperature:
1. layers or strata become **folded bands**
2. rounded grains become **crystals**.

Important features
- banding
- crystals of various sizes

Changes depend on conditions
High pressure is always needed for metamorphosis, but the
temperature may vary.

e.g. shale → slate (high P)
high P → schist
high P → gneiss

increasing
temperature

IGNEOUS ROCKS

Minerals are naturally occurring metal compounds.

Ores are rocks from which metals can be extracted in
economic quantities. Ores contain minerals or (sometimes)
metals.

Iron ore contains the mineral **haematite**. **Aluminium ore**
contains the mineral **bauxite**. **Gold ore** contains **gold metal**.

Extrusive igneous rocks
These are formed from
magma which solidifies **on
Earth's surface.**
e.g. basalt
They cool quickly forming
small crystals or a glass.

Intrusive igneous rocks
These are formed from
magma which solidifies
inside Earth's crust.
e.g. granite
They cool slowly forming
larger crystals.

Igneous rocks are rocks of
volcanic origin. They form when
magma (molten rock from inside
Earth) cools and solidifies. The
speed of cooling controls the
crystal size.

Important features
- crystalline

Lava

IGNEOUS ROCKS

Melting

MAGMA

From mantle

The structure of Earth and the theory of tectonic plates

TECTONIC PLATE THEORY

This states that the continents are made of less dense crustal rock floating on plates of the mantle. These plates move because there are convection currents in the inner part of Earth.

Evidence for tectonic plate theory

1. Continental coastlines fit together like bits of a jigsaw. e.g. the coasts of Africa and South America match each other.

2. There are similar rocks on either side of the oceans which match when the continents are moved together. e.g. similar rocks and fossils are found in Africa and South America.

3. Geological evidence of climatic change suggests that plates have moved. e.g. desert sands, tropical fossils, and glacial deposits show that Britain has moved on Earth's surface.

4. Position of mountain chains and island arcs. e.g. Japan and the Philippines show where plate margins are meeting.

5. Magnetic record preserved in rocks: magnetic stripes and wandering north pole. e.g. parallel lines of magnetism on either side of mid-ocean ridges show that there has been sea-floor spreading.

EVIDENCE FOR EARTH'S STRUCTURE

1. **Volcanoes**
   They indicate that the inside of Earth is hot and under pressure.

2. **Earthquakes**
   A pattern of shock waves spreads out through Earth from an earthquake. The pattern made by the waves tells us about the structure of Earth.

EARTH'S STRUCTURE

Studying earthquake waves tells us that Earth has a layered structure made of:

- a **very thin crust** a few tens of kilometres thick
- the **mantle** of underlying rock about 6000 km thick
- a **liquid core** about 2000 km thick
- a **solid core** about 1000 km thick in the centre.

Crust
Inner core (solid)
Outer core (liquid)
Mantle

Destructive plate margins and mountain building

At these margins two plates moving in the opposite direction meet. One plate is forced under the other in a process called **subduction**. Lighter continental rock floating on the plates also collides. It piles up making mountains (e.g. the Himalayas). The movement of one plate past the other causes earthquakes.

Constructive plate margins

At these margins new, dense, dark, igneous rock (basalt) rises from the mantle forming ridges of new mountains and volcanoes in the middle of the oceans. These are called **mid-ocean ridges**. Iceland is the northern end of a mid-ocean ridge which runs down the middle of the Atlantic Ocean. The new, hot, liquid rock rises up and pushes older rock aside causing **sea-floor spreading**. As the molten rock solidifies, its magnetism is set in the direction of the north pole. Because Earth's magnetism has reversed a number of times, earlier rocks have their magnetism set in the opposite direction. So the rocks contain a striped pattern of magnetism.

Destructive plate margins and island arcs

Sometimes two plates collide under the sea where the continental crust is very thin. Here the dense basaltic rock slides under the lighter continental rock (subduction). This causes earthquakes. Volcanoes also form because the crust is so thin. These volcanoes produce rocks which are lighter in colour and density than those in the mid-ocean ridges (e.g. granite). The volcanoes lie in an arc along the line of the plate collision. Because they are in the ocean they form an arc of islands (e.g. Japan, the Philippines).

Continental rock
Subduction
Magma
newer older
Subduction
Lithosphere
Asthenosphere

Conservative margins

When the edges of two plates move past each other without either plate going underneath, faults and earthquakes happen. No plates are destroyed or made, so this boundary between plates is called a conservative margin. Examples include the San Andreas fault in California, and the Jordan Valley.

Mediterranean Sea
Sea of Galilee
Dead Sea
Arabian Plate
African Plate

Materials from rocks: limestone and its uses

■ Calcium carbonate rocks

BUILDING MATERIAL
Limestone is a **hard sedimentary rock**. It is used for road foundations and to make buildings.

MAKING CEMENT
Limestone and clay are heated together in a furnace to make cement.

$$4CaCO_3(s) + Al_2Si_2O_7(s) \rightarrow$$
$$2CaSiO_3(s) + Ca_2Al_2O_5(s) + 4CO_2(g)$$

cement

MAKING GLASS
Limestone, sand, and sodium carbonate are heated together to make glass. This **soda glass** is used in windows. Soda glasses have the follow range of compositions:

SiO_2	70–75%
Na_2O	12–16%
CaO	5–11%

If boron oxide is added to the reaction mixture, a **borosilicate glass** is produced. Borosilicate glasses are harder than soda glasses and can be heated without softening. Pyrex is a borosilicate glass.

LIMESTONE QUARRY

MINING AND QUARRYING
These processes:
* create ugly slag heaps and scar the landscape
* generate a lot of heavy traffic
* cause dust and smoke pollution

but also
* provide jobs and income
* provide valuable raw materials.

NEUTRALIZING LAKES
Limestone (calcium carbonate) is a **base**. It neutralizes lakes made acid by acid rain. Powdered limestone can be sprayed onto lakes for this purpose.

MAKING LIME FOR AGRICULTURE
Metal carbonates decompose on heating. Heating limestone produces **quicklime** which reacts with water to make **slaked lime**.

$$CaCO_3(s) \xrightarrow{\text{heat}} CaO(s) + CO_2(g)$$
$$\text{quicklime}$$

$$CaO(s) + H_2O(l) \rightarrow Ca(OH)_2(s)$$
$$\text{slaked lime}$$

MAKING IRON
Limestone is mixed with iron ore and coke to form the 'charge' which is loaded into a **blast furnace** (see p. 45). The limestone reacts with the high melting point non-metal impurities in the iron ore. It forms a molten slag which floats on top of the iron.

Iron and steel

MANUFACTURE OF IRON

There is less iron than aluminium in Earth's crust, but it is easier and cheaper to extract.

The main ore is **haematite**, Fe_2O_3.

Iron is below zinc in the reactivity list so it forms fairly reactive compounds. Iron is extracted from haematite by **reducing it with carbon in a blast furnace**.

The **charge** is loaded into the top of the furnace.

The charge contains:
- iron ore – source of iron
- coke – fuel and reducing agent
- limestone – to form a **slag** by dissolving the high melting point non-metal impurities.

REACTIONS

1. **The coke burns**
   $$C(s) + O_2(g) \rightarrow CO_2(g)$$

2. **More coke reduces the carbon dioxide**
   $$CO_2(g) + C(s) \rightarrow 2CO(g)$$

3. **Carbon monoxide reduces iron ore**
   $$Fe_2O_3(s) + 3CO(g) \rightarrow 2Fe(l) + 3CO_2(g)$$

4. **Carbon reduces iron ore**
   $$2Fe_2O_3(s) + 3C(s) \rightarrow 4Fe(l) + 3CO_2(g)$$

5. **Limestone decomposes**
   $$CaCO_3(s) \rightarrow CaO(s) + CO_2(g)$$

6. **Slag forms**
   $$CaO(s) + SiO_2(s) \rightarrow CaSiO_3(l)$$

furnace gas

400°C

800°C

1400°C

charge

limestone + ore

coke

slag

pig iron

iron

slag

A **blast of hot air** goes into the bottom.

'Pig' iron is produced. This contains C, Si, S, P. It is very brittle.

RUSTING

$$4Fe(s) + 3O_2(g) + 6H_2O(l) \rightarrow 4\,Fe(OH)_3(s) \rightarrow 2\,\underset{\text{rust}}{Fe_2O_3.6H_2O(s)}$$

Simple lab experiments show:

1. That air and water are needed for iron to rust. So rusting is an **oxidation reaction**.

   (a) control
   (b) air and water – nail rusts
   (c) boiled water with oil on top – no rust
   (d) drying agent + air – no rust

2. Iron rusts when in contact with a less reactive metal, but not when in contact with a more reactive metal.

copper — lots of rust

zinc — no rust

Stopping rust

1. **Coat the iron**: paint, oil or grease, chrome plate. This prevents air and water meeting the iron.
2. **Sacrificial protection**: galvanizing (zinc plating) or zinc anodes. The zinc reacts instead of the iron, so the iron is protected.
3. **Alloying**: e.g. stainless steel. Alloying modifies the reactivity of the iron.

STEEL MAKING

Pig iron is too brittle to be useful. It is turned into steel by:
1. mixing the molten iron with 30% scrap steel
2. blowing oxygen through to burn out impurities
3. adding weighed amounts of alloying elements.

oxygen lance

Aluminium extraction

Conditions
950°C
4–5 volts
100 000 amps

Alumina hopper

HALL CELL

Graphite
anode

Molten
aluminium

Alumina
in cryolite

Graphite-lined
steel cathode

Inputs
- bauxite: source of aluminium
- carbon: for anodes, which get burnt
- cryolite: to lower m.p. (this is mainly recycled)
- electricity: which makes this an expensive process

Aluminium is a reactive metal so it is extracted using **electrolysis**. (Aluminium appears to be unreactive, but only because it is protected by an oxide layer.)

The ore of aluminium is the mineral **bauxite**, Al_2O_3. It is purified in its country of origin to reduce transport costs.

Alumina, purified aluminium oxide, has a very high melting point (2045°C). This is lowered by adding an impurity called **cryolite**, Na_3AlF_6.

The impure aluminium oxide is electrolysed in the **Hall cell**. The electrolyte is kept molten by the heating effect of the huge current.

USES OF ALUMINIUM
The uses of aluminium depend on its properties:
- it is strong but light: used for planes, window frames
- conducts quite well: used for cables
- protected by oxide layer: boat fittings, saucepans

CATHODE REACTION

$Al^{3+}(l) + 3e^- \rightarrow Al(l)$

ANODE REACTION

$2O^{2-}(l) \rightarrow O_2(g) + 4e^-$
$C(s) + O_2(g) \rightarrow CO_2(g)$

Copper extraction and purification

Conditions
0.25 volts
800 amps

Impure copper anode

Pure copper cathode

Electrolyte of sulphuric acid and copper sulphate

Anode sludge

Copper is an unreactive metal so its compounds are quite reactive.

Copper is **extracted by smelting** – roasting or heating – the ore in a furnace.

Unlike a blast furnace the ore does not come into contact with the carbon fuel.

The copper produced is very impure.

Most of the properties of copper, such as electrical conduction and malleability, depend on the metal being very pure. So copper is **purified using electrolysis**.

ANODE REACTION
Copper atoms are oxidized to ions

$Cu(s) \rightarrow Cu^{2+}(aq) + 2e^-$

Each reaction is the exact reverse of the other. So the result is that copper is transferred from the impure anode to the 99.99% pure cathode. This method can also be used to plate copper onto other metals.

If the voltage is accurately controlled, only copper is deposited on the cathode. Other metals fall to the bottom forming anode sludge. Platinum, gold, silver, molybdenum, selenium, and tellurium are all extracted from the sludge.

CATHODE REACTION
Copper cations are reduced to metal

$Cu^{2+}(aq) + 2e^- \rightarrow Cu(s)$

Transition elements

TITANIUM

Extraction

Titanium is very expensive to extract because it is extracted by a batch process instead of a continuous one.

Titanium is displaced from purified titanium chloride by magnesium, a more reactive metal.

$$TiCl_4(l) + 2Mg(l) \rightarrow Ti(s) + 2\,MgCl_2(l)$$

Uses

Titanium is light but very strong. It is used in making turbine blades, aeroplane parts, and artificial limbs.

Once a **continuous process** is started up, metal is made continuously until the process is stopped. In a **batch process**, the furnace is loaded and heated up, reaction takes place, then the furnace is cooled down and unloaded. This whole process is then repeated. This wastes energy and time.

The transition elements are found between Groups 2 and 3 of the periodic table. They have characteristic properties (see p. 18). They also have a wide range of uses which depend on these properties.

COPPER, SILVER, AND GOLD

These are all easy to extract, but silver and gold are rare and so expensive. They all show typical metallic properties (good electrical conductivity, malleable, ductile). Their uses follow from their properties.

Copper

- is widely used as an electrical conductor (cheap, good electrical conductivity). But it is now being replaced by aluminium – which is cheaper and lighter– for cables in the electricity grid.
- is used for pipes (unreactive, ductile)
- is used for coins (unreactive, has a distinctive colour)

Silver and gold

- are sometimes used to coat electrical contacts, where the heat of sparking would cause copper to oxidize (unreactive, good electrical conductivity)
- are used for jewellery (rare, precious, attractive colours)

ZINC, CHROMIUM, NICKEL, AND COPPER

The biggest disadvantage of iron and steel is that they rust. Replacing or repairing rusting structures costs huge amounts every year. Rusting can be prevented by:

- galvanizing or coating the iron with zinc
- alloying the iron with a less reactive metal (e.g. chromium or nickel)
- chrome-plating steel, which provides a decorative, unreactive surface. But the steel will rust badly if the chrome layer is scratched through, because chromium is less reactive than iron.

Brass is sometimes used instead of iron. It is an alloy of copper and zinc.

Ti		Cr	Mn	Fe		Ni	Cu	Zn
							Ag	
							Au	

Steel

When iron is purified and alloyed with small amounts of carbon, steel is made. The amount of carbon changes the properties of the steel.

- **mild steel** (0.09–0.2% carbon): malleable and not very hard; used for car bodies, cans, nails, wire
- **high carbon steel** (0.4–0.9% carbon): harder and less malleable; used for tools, masonry nails

Alloy steels

The properties of steel can be further changed by adding other transition metals:

- **stainless steel** is 18% chromium, 8% nickel
- **manganese steel** is very strong and hard; used for drill bits, cutting tools, springs.

IRON

Cast iron is brittle but hard because of the impurities it contains. It is used for making manhole covers.

Chemicals from salt

Common salt, sodium chloride, is found naturally:

1. dissolved in **sea water** (about 2.6% in a typical sample) from which it is extracted by **evaporation**;
2. as **rock salt**, a sedimentary evaporite. There are huge deposits of rock salt in Cheshire. These are extracted by **solution mining**.

Sodium is a very reactive metal so it is extracted by **electrolysis**. Chlorine is also very reactive. The cells used for electrolysis are designed to keep the very reactive products apart.

Uses of sodium chloride

- added to food to preserve it (ham)
- put on icy roads to melt the ice
- a source of sodium, chlorine, and sodium hydroxide

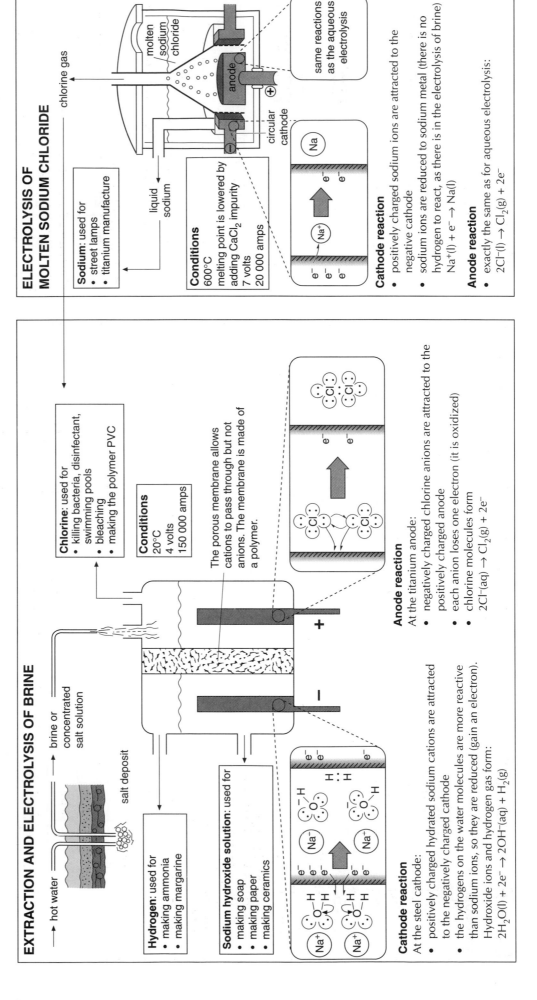

ELECTROLYSIS OF MOLTEN SODIUM CHLORIDE

Sodium: used for
- street lamps
- titanium manufacture

Conditions
600°C
melting point is lowered by adding $CaCl_2$ impurity
7 volts
20 000 amps

same reactions as the aqueous electrolysis

Cathode reaction
- positively charged sodium ions are attracted to the negative cathode
- sodium ions are reduced to sodium metal (there is no hydrogen to react, as there is in the electrolysis of brine)
  $Na^+(l) + e^- \rightarrow Na(l)$

Anode reaction
- exactly the same as for aqueous electrolysis:
  $2Cl^-(l) \rightarrow Cl_2(g) + 2e^-$

EXTRACTION AND ELECTROLYSIS OF BRINE

hot water → brine or concentrated salt solution

salt deposit

Chlorine: used for
- killing bacteria, disinfectant, swimming pools
- bleaching
- making the polymer PVC

Conditions
20°C
4 volts
150 000 amps

The porous membrane allows cations to pass through but not anions. The membrane is made of a polymer.

Hydrogen: used for
- making ammonia
- making margarine

Sodium hydroxide solution: used for
- making soap
- making paper
- making ceramics

Anode reaction
At the titanium anode:
- negatively charged chlorine anions are attracted to the positively charged anode
- each anion loses one electron (it is oxidized)
- chlorine molecules form
  $2Cl^-(aq) \rightarrow Cl_2(g) + 2e^-$

Cathode reaction
At the steel cathode:
- positively charged hydrated sodium cations are attracted to the negatively charged cathode
- the hydrogens on the water molecules are more reactive than sodium ions, so they are reduced (gain an electron).
  Hydroxide ions and hydrogen gas form:
  $2H_2O(l) + 2e^- \rightarrow 2OH^-(aq) + H_2(g)$

Chemicals from crude oil

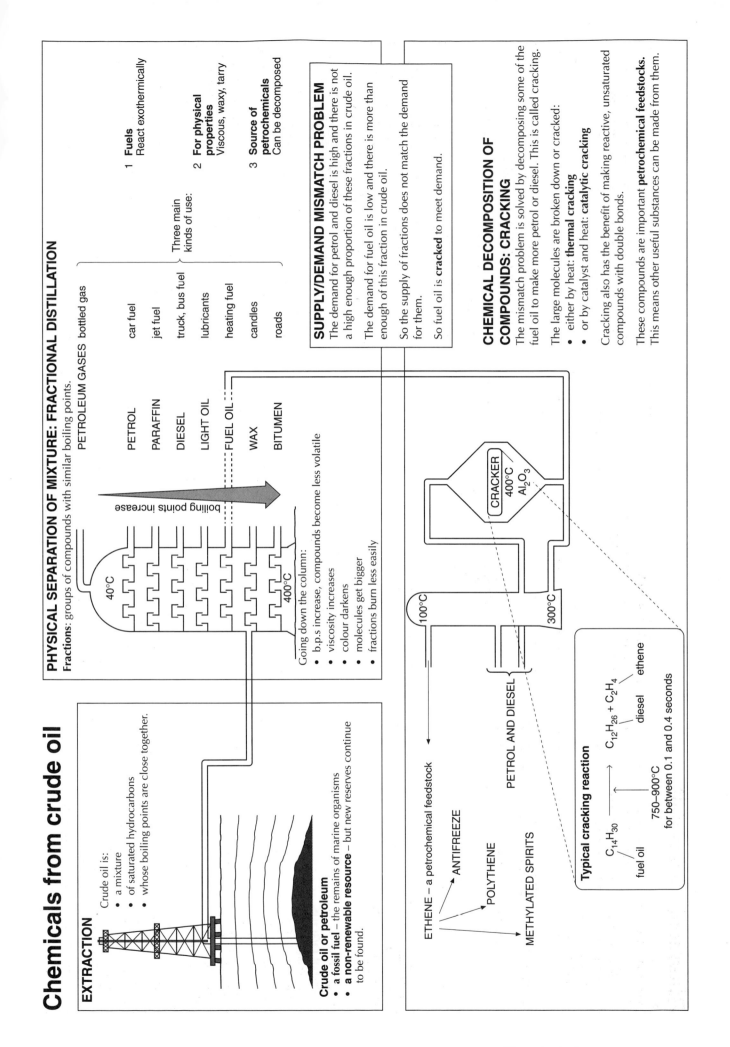

EXTRACTION

Crude oil is:
- a mixture
- of saturated hydrocarbons
- whose boiling points are close together.

Crude oil or petroleum
- **a fossil fuel** – the remains of marine organisms
- **a non-renewable resource** – but new reserves continue to be found.

PHYSICAL SEPARATION OF MIXTURE: FRACTIONAL DISTILLATION

Fractions: groups of compounds with similar boiling points.

PETROLEUM GASES bottled gas

PETROL car fuel

PARAFFIN jet fuel

DIESEL truck, bus fuel

LIGHT OIL lubricants

FUEL OIL heating fuel

WAX candles

BITUMEN roads

boiling points increase

40°C

400°C

Going down the column:
- b.p.s increase, compounds become less volatile
- viscosity increases
- colour darkens
- molecules get bigger
- fractions burn less easily

Three main kinds of use:

1 **Fuels**
   React exothermically

2 **For physical properties**
   Viscous, waxy, tarry

3 **Source of petrochemicals**
   Can be decomposed

SUPPLY/DEMAND MISMATCH PROBLEM

The demand for petrol and diesel is high and there is not a high enough proportion of these fractions in crude oil.

The demand for fuel oil is low and there is more than enough of this fraction in crude oil.

So the supply of fractions does not match the demand for them.

So fuel oil is **cracked** to meet demand.

CHEMICAL DECOMPOSITION OF COMPOUNDS: CRACKING

The mismatch problem is solved by decomposing some of the fuel oil to make more petrol or diesel. This is called cracking.

The large molecules are broken down or cracked:
- either by heat: **thermal cracking**
- or by catalyst and heat: **catalytic cracking**

Cracking also has the benefit of making reactive, unsaturated compounds with double bonds.

These compounds are important **petrochemical feedstocks.** This means other useful substances can be made from them.

CRACKER
400°C
Al_2O_3

100°C

300°C

PETROL AND DIESEL

ETHENE – a petrochemical feedstock

ANTIFREEZE

POLYTHENE

METHYLATED SPIRITS

Typical cracking reaction

$$C_{14}H_{30} \longrightarrow C_{12}H_{26} + C_2H_4$$

fuel oil   diesel   ethene

750–900°C for between 0.1 and 0.4 seconds

Alkanes

- contain only carbon and hydrogen
- contain only single covalent bonds
- have the maximum amount of hydrogen bonded to the carbon skeleton
- are described as saturated

Name	Molecular formula	Structural formula
methane	CH_4	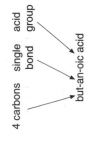
ethane	C_2H_6 or CH_3CH_3	
propane	C_3H_8 or $CH_3CH_2CH_3$	
butane	C_4H_{10} or $CH_3CH_2CH_2CH_3$	
pentane	C_5H_{12} or $CH_3CH_2CH_2CH_2CH_3$	

HOMOLOGOUS SERIES

The alkanes are an example of a **homologous series.**

A homologous series is a group of compounds:

1. with the same general formula – the alkanes have the formula C_nH_{2n+2} where n is the number of carbon atoms
2. each of which differs from the next by $-CH_2-$
3. which show a gradual trend in physical properties
4. which have the same chemical reactions.

All the alkanes burn in air.
e.g. $C_3H_8 + 5O_2 \rightarrow 3CO_2 + 4H_2O$

NAMING IN ORGANIC CHEMISTRY

The names of compounds have three parts:

First part: gives the length of the carbon chain

1 carbon → meth-; 2 carbons → eth-; 3 carbons → prop-; 4 carbons → but-

Second part: tells whether there are any double or triple bonds in the carbon chain

all single bonds → -an-; a double bond → -en-; a triple bond -yn-

Third part (ending): tells what is joined to the carbon chain

only hydrogen → -e; a hydroxyl group → -ol; an acid group → -oic acid.

e.g.

2 carbons   single   hydroxyl
            bond   group
→ eth-an-ol

3 carbons   double   only
            bond   H
→ prop-en-e

4 carbons   single   acid
            bond   group
→ but-an-oic acid

ISOMERISM

The atoms of alkanes from butane upwards can be bonded together in more than one way. This is called **isomerism.**

Isomers are molecules with the *same molecular formula but different structural formulas.*

e.g. butane C_4H_{10} can be:

1. a straight chain

2. a branched chain

STRUCTURE AND BOILING POINTS

As the graph shows, the longer the chain of carbon atoms, the higher the boiling point. This is because longer chain molecules have bigger forces holding them together.

But the more branched the chain the lower the boiling point, because branched chains cannot pack together so tightly.

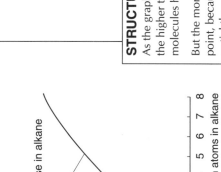

steady increase in alkane boiling points

Boiling point /°C

Number of carbon atoms in alkane

Alkenes

- contain only carbon and hydrogen
- have a double bond between two of the carbon atoms
- do not have the maximum amount of hydrogen bonded to the carbon skeleton
- are described as unsaturated

$$H \diagdown C = C \diagup H$$
$$H \diagup \qquad \diagdown H$$

Name	Molecular formula	Structural formula
ethene	C_2H_4 or $CH_2{=}CH_2$	H—C=C—H (with H on each carbon)
propene	C_3H_6 or $CH_3CH{=}CH_2$	structural formula of propene
butene	C_4H_8 or $CH_3CH_2CH{=}CH_2$ or $CH_3CH{=}CHCH_3$	structural formulae of butene (two isomers) and

ANOTHER HOMOLOGOUS SERIES

- general formula C_nH_{2n} where n is the number of carbon atoms
- physical properties show a steady trend as chain length increases
- more stable than alkanes when heated alone (stronger bonding)
- more reactive than alkanes when added to other substances.

ADDITION REACTIONS

Alkenes combine with bromine, hydrogen, water, and even themselves. These combination reactions are called **additions.**

1. Reaction with bromine

If an alkene is shaken with bromine water, the orange colour of the bromine disappears as the bromine reacts with the alkene.

$$H_2C{=}CH_2 + Br{-}Br \rightarrow H{-}C{-}C{-}H$$

colourless   orange   colourless

This reaction is used to distinguish between alkanes and alkenes. If an alkane is shaken with bromine water the colour of the bromine does not go.

2. Reaction with hydrogen

In the presence of a nickel catalyst, hydrogen adds on to an alkene making an alkane.

$$H_2C{=}CH_2 + H_2 \xrightarrow[180^\circ C]{Ni} \quad (ethane)$$

This reaction is important for making vegetable oil into fat.

3. Reaction with water

Ethene reacts with water making ethanol (an alcohol).

$$H_2C{=}CH_2 + H{-}OH \xrightarrow[\substack{300^\circ C \\ 70\ atmospheres}]{H_3PO_4\ catalyst} H{-}C{-}C{-}H$$

4. Reaction with more ethene

Under suitable conditions, ethene molecules react with each other, linking up to form a long chain molecule. This process is called **polymerization.** The ethene reactants are monomers; the long chain product is a polymer.

$$\xrightarrow{Ziegler\ catalyst}$$

monomers   part of a polymer chain

OILS AND FATS

Vegetable oils and animal fats are similar compounds but with one important difference. Vegetable oils contain carbon–carbon double bonds: they are **unsaturated.** Animal fats contain only carbon–carbon single bonds: they are **saturated.** Vegetable oils contain carbon–carbon single bonds. This makes them saturated like animal fats.

Vegetable oils are turned into fats by reacting them with hydrogen. This makes them saturated like animal fats. The process is called **hardening.**

It is cheaper to make fat from vegetable oils in this way than to get fats from animals.

'Hardened' vegetable oils are sold as margarine.

Alcohols

HOMOLOGOUS SERIES

Alcohols are a homologous series with the general formula $C_nH_{2n+1}OH$.

The first three members are:

methanol CH_3OH

ethanol CH_3CH_2OH

propanol $CH_3CH_2CH_2OH$

Ethanol is the most important alcohol.

INDUSTRIAL MANUFACTURE OF ETHANOL

Ethanol is made by adding water to ethene. This reaction is called **hydration** and is an *addition* reaction.

$$CH_2{=}CH_2(g) + H_2O(g) \xrightarrow[\substack{300^\circ C \\ 70\ atmospheres}]{H_3PO_4} CH_3CH_2OH(l)$$

This process:
- is continuous
- produces pure ethanol
- uses finite resources (crude oil)
- produces large volumes cheaply

The alcohol produced by this method is '**methylated**' by adding methanol. This makes it undrinkable so people cannot drink industrial ethanol and avoid paying duty on the alcohol they drink.

Uses of methylated spirits

Industrial ethanol is sold as methylated spirits. It is used:
- as a fuel
- as a solvent

Hydrocarbon chain with an end like water

- Like water it has hydrogen bonding. So it is miscible with (soluble in) water.
- Like water it reacts with sodium giving off hydrogen:
  $2CH_3CH_2OH(l) + 2Na(s) \rightarrow 2CH_3CH_2ONa(s) + H_2(g)$

ETHANOL

FERMENTATION

Alcohol for drinking is made by **fermenting** carbohydrates. This is an example of an enzyme-catalysed reaction.

$$C_{12}H_{22}O_{11}(s) + H_2O(l) \xrightarrow{yeast} 2C_6H_{12}O_6(aq)$$
sucrose

$$C_6H_{12}O_6(aq) \xrightarrow{yeast} 2CH_3CH_2OH(l) + 2CO_2(g)$$
glucose

This process:
- is a batch process
- produces impure alcohol
- uses renewable resources
- produces relatively small volumes
- is enzyme-catalysed anaerobic decomposition of the carbohydrate

The impurities produced give drinks like beer, wine, and whisky their own special tastes and flavours.

FUEL

- Like ethene, ethanol burns making carbon dioxide and water and giving out energy:
  $CH_3CH_2OH(l) + 3O_2(g) \rightarrow 2CO_2(g) + 3H_2O(l)$

This is **complete oxidation** or **combustion**.

PARTIAL OXIDATION

In aqueous solution ethanol can be **partially oxidized** to ethanoic acid.
- In the home this happens when wine is left open to the air (the wine goes sour).
- In the lab this happens when ethanol is warmed with an oxidizing agent, e.g. potassium dichromate(VI) in dilute acid.

$$CH_3CH_2OH(l) \xrightarrow{K_2Cr_2O_7/H^+} CH_3COOH(l)$$
ethanol — ethanoic acid

ALCOHOL CONTENT OF DRINKS

Spirits	~40%
Fortified wine	>17%
Wine	8–17%
Beer	~5%

Many people enjoy alcoholic drinks. But it is important to keep alcohol consumption within sensible limits, as it can have some harmful effects.
- Alcohol affects people's reaction times and co-ordination. So there is a legal limit on the amount of alcohol which may be drunk before driving.
- Alcohol can be damaging to health. Too much causes dizziness and vomiting. Over time it can damage the liver. Some people become dependent on alcohol.

Carboxylic acids

HOMOLOGOUS SERIES

The carboxylic acids form a homologous series.

The first three are:

methanoic acid   CHOOH

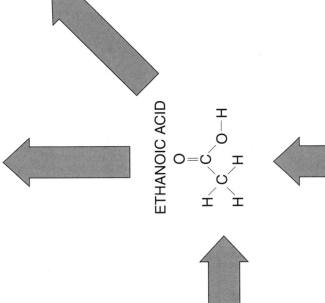

ethanoic acid CH_3COOH

propanoic acid CH_3CH_2COOH

MAKING ETHANOIC ACID

Ethanoic acid is made by the partial oxidation of ethanol. Compare this with the complete oxidation.

Partial oxidation
$$CH_3CH_2OH(l) + 2[O] \rightarrow CH_3COOH(l) + H_2O(l)$$

Complete oxidation
$$CH_3CH_2OH(l) + 3O_2(g) \rightarrow 2CO_2(g) + 3H_2O(l)$$

Partial oxidation is performed in solution in a test tube or beaker. The oxygen for the oxidation is supplied by acidified potassium dichromate(VI), which is a strong oxidizing agent. The reaction is slow unless it is heated.

Potassium dichromate(VI) is orange. The solution goes *green* during the reaction.

orange colour   changes to   green colour

warm

ethanol and potassium dichromate in dilute sulphuric acid

ethanoic acid

USES

- used in making textiles
- vinegar is impure ethanoic acid.

ETHANOIC ACID

TYPICAL REACTIONS

1. With water
Carboxylic acids react with water forming hydrogen ions. They are *weak acids*, so they only form a few ions; most of the molecules remain as molecules.

e.g. $CH_3COOH(l) + H_2O(l) \rightleftharpoons CH_3COO^-(aq) + H^+(aq)$
       99.9% molecules   0.1% ions

So the dissociation of the acid in water is incomplete.

2. With universal indicator
Carboxylic acids change the colour of universal indicator. They are weak acids so the indicator goes *orange*. (With strong acids the indicator goes red.)

3. With reactive metals
Carboxylic acids react with reactive metals like magnesium:

$$Mg(s) + 2CH_3COOH(aq) \rightarrow Mg(CH_3COO)_2(aq) + H_2(g)$$

4. With bases
Carboxylic acids are neutralized by bases such as sodium hydroxide or sodium carbonate:

$$CH_3COOH(aq) + NaOH(aq) \rightarrow CH_3COONa(aq) + H_2O(l)$$
$$2CH_3COOH(aq) + Na_2CO_3(aq) \rightarrow 2CH_3COONa(aq) + CO_2(g) + H_2O(l)$$

5. With alcohols
Carboxylic acids react with alcohols. A molecule of acid reacts with a molecule of alcohol, splitting out water and making a substance called an **ester**.

$$CH_3CO OH(l) + HOCH_2CH_3(l) \rightleftharpoons CH_3COOCH_2CH_3(l) + H_2O(l)$$
   acid   +   alcohol   ester   +   water

This reaction is *reversible* and *very slow*. It is catalysed by concentrated sulphuric acid.

Esters have fruity smells and flavours. They are used in the food industry.

Polymers

These are very large, usually long-chain molecules made by linking together huge numbers of small molecules called **monomers**.

$$n\,A \rightarrow -A-A-A-A-$$

monomers → polymer

NATURAL POLYMERS

Plants take in small molecules and build large molecules from them. Animals take in large molecules (by eating plants or other animals), break them down by digestion, then build new large molecules from them.

Carbohydrates

Glucose is made by photosynthesis:

$$6\,CO_{2(g)} + 6\,H_2O_{(2)} \rightarrow 6\,O_{2(g)} + C_6H_{12}O_6$$

glucose

Glucose is then linked to make starch or cellulose:

$$n\ \text{H} \qquad \text{OH} \rightarrow \text{H}$$

starch

Proteins

Amino acids link up to make **proteins**:

$$n\ NH_2\,CHCOOH \rightarrow$$

CONDENSATION POLYMERS

This group of polymers is made by linking up molecules which are reactive at each end, such as amino acids:

$$n\ NH_2 \text{\raise1pt\hbox{$\sim$}} COOH \rightarrow NH_2 \text{\raise1pt\hbox{$\sim$}} C=O \quad \text{...} \quad + n\,H_2O$$

carbon chain

Each time two molecules join together, a small molecule (often water) is also formed as atoms are pushed out to make room for new bonds. This water condenses on the walls of the reaction vessel, so these are called **condensation polymers**.

Nylon and **polyester** are examples of condensation polymers.

ADDITION POLYMERS

Chemists have imitated nature by linking together small molecules to make new materials.

Addition polymers are made from *unsaturated* monomers.

double bond is made into two single bonds.

MONOMER		POLYMER	
$H_2C=CH_2$	ethene	$-(CH_2-CH_2)-_n$	polythene – poly(ethene) – used for bags, sheets, bottles
$H_2C=CHCH_3$	propene	$-(CH_2-CH(CH_3))-_n$	polypropene used for crates, ropes
$H_2C=CHCl$	vinyl chloride (chloroethene)	$-(CH_2-CHCl)-_n$	polyvinylchloride(PVC) used for coats, hoses, bottles
$H_2C=CHC_6H_5$	styrene	$-(CH_2-CHC_6H_5)-_n$	polystyrene used for foams, electrical insulation

THERMOSOFTENING AND THERMOSETTING POLYMERS

Thermosoftening plastics

Some polymers (e.g. polythene, nylon) soften when heated and harden when cooled. This process can be repeated as often as needed. These are called **thermosoftening** plastics.

Thermosets or thermosetting plastics

Other polymers soften when heated but then new bonds form between the chains and the polymer hardens permanently. It will not soften again. These are called **thermosetting** polymers.

tangled chains

heat

chains now bonded with new cross-links

Relative masses and moles

MASS NUMBER

These are the masses of atoms compared to each other expressed on a scale on which the carbon-12 isotope has a mass of exactly 12 units.

^{12}C is the standard

0 1 2 3 4 5 6 7 8 9 10 11 12 13 14 15 16 17 18 19 20 atomic mass scale

AVOGADRO NUMBER OR AVOGADRO CONSTANT

The number of atoms in exactly 12 g of carbon-12 can be counted.

The **Avogadro number** is the number of atoms in exactly 12 g of the isotope ^{12}C. It is found to be 6×10^{23}.

6×10^{23} atoms

THE MOLE

Chemists measure the **amount** of any substance in moles.

A **mole** of any substance is the amount which contains the same number of particles of the substance as there are atoms in 12 g of ^{12}C.

i.e. it is the Avogadro number of particles of that substance.

Amount	1 mole of carbon	1 mole of magnesium	1 mole of water
	contains	contains	contains
Number	6×10^{23} carbon atoms	6×10^{23} magnesium atoms	6×10^{23} water molecules
	have mass	have mass	have mass
Mass	12 g of carbon	24 g of magnesium	18 g of water

The mass of 1 mole (the **molar mass**) is the same as the formula mass in grams.

NATURALLY OCCURRING ELEMENTS AND RELATIVE ATOMIC MASS

All naturally occurring elements are mixtures of isotopes.

e.g. chlorine
75% ^{35}Cl
25% ^{37}Cl

$$\frac{(75 \times 35) + (25 \times 37)}{100} = 35.5$$

Mass of an *average* chlorine atom is 35.5 on ^{12}C scale.

atomic mass scale

Relative atomic mass is the weighted average of the masses of the naturally occurring isotopes of an element on the ^{12}C scale. These values are usually rounded off to the nearest whole number. Symbol A_r.

RELATIVE FORMULA MASS AND PERCENTAGE COMPOSITION

The **relative formula mass** is the sum of the relative atomic masses in the formula. Symbol M_r.

e.g. carbon dioxide, CO_2

12 + 16 + 16 → 44

e.g. sodium chloride, NaCl

23 + 35.5 → 58.5

% Composition

$\% C = \dfrac{12}{44} \times 100 = 27.3\%$

$\% O = \dfrac{16 + 16}{44} \times 100 = 72.7\%$

i.e. $\dfrac{\text{mass of element}}{\text{total mass}} \times 100$

KEY RELATIONSHIP

$$\text{Amount of substance in moles} = \frac{\text{mass of substance in g}}{\text{mass of 1 mole in g}}$$

Using moles

CHANGING MOLES TO MASS
Key relationship

number of moles $\times$ molar mass = mass in g

N.B. **A mole of oxygen** can mean two things. It can mean
- 1 mole of oxygen atoms which weighs 16 g or
- 1 mole of oxygen molecules which weighs 32 g.

So *always say what particles you are referring to.*

WORKED EXAMPLES
What is the mass of 1.5 moles of magnesium?
$1.5 \times 24 = 36$ g

What is the mass of 0.75 moles of copper(II) oxide?
$0.75 \times (64 + 16) = 0.75 \times 80 = 60$ g

CHANGING MASS TO MOLES
Key relationship

$$\frac{\text{mass in grams}}{\text{molar mass}} = \text{number of moles}$$

WORKED EXAMPLES
How many moles in 10 g of calcium?
$\frac{10}{40} = 0.25$ mol

How many moles in 10 g of calcium carbonate, $CaCO_3$?
$\frac{10}{40 + 12 + (16 \times 3)} = \frac{10}{100} = 0.1$ mol

FINDING FORMULAS FROM PERCENTAGE COMPOSITION FIGURES

Use the relationship above to work out the relative number of moles of each element. Then work out the ratio of moles of each element. This formula, which only gives you the *whole number ratio* of atoms is called the **empirical formula**.

To work out the *actual* number of atoms in the molecule (the **molecular formula**), you also have to know the relative formula mass.

Process
1. Assume you have 100g and turn % figures into grams.
2. Convert these masses into moles.
3. Divide these figures by the smallest to get formula.

WORKED EXAMPLES
What is the empirical formula of a hydrocarbon which is 85.7% carbon and 14.3 % hydrogen? Its relative molar mass is 42. What is its molecular formula?
Assume you have 100 g of the hydrocarbon.

The masses are:
carbon 85.7 g   hydrogen 14.3 g

The moles are:
carbon 85.7/12   hydrogen 14.3/1
$= 7.14$ mol $= 14.3$ mol

The simplest ratio of moles is found by dividing by the smallest:
7.14/7.14 $= 1$ 14.3/7.14 $= 2$

so the empirical formula is C_1H_2.

The formula mass of $C_1H_2 = 12 + 2 = 14$.

The formula mass of the hydrocarbon is 42 which = 3 $\times$ empirical formula mass,

so the molecular formula is C_3H_6.

A compound has the percentage composition: sodium 29.1%; sulphur 40.5 %; oxygen 30.4%. Its relative formula mass is 158. What is its formula?

	Na	S	O
% composition	29.1	40.5	30.4

Assume you have 100 g of the compound.

The masses are:

	29.1 g	40.5 g	30.4 g

The moles are:

	29.1/23	40.5/32	30.4/16
	= 1.27 mol	= 1.27 mol	= 1.9 mol

Divided by the smaller number :

	1.27/1.27	:	1.27/1.27	:	1.9/1.27
	= 1	:	1	:	1.5

There must be whole numbers of atoms, so this becomes

2   :   2   :   3

The empirical formula is $Na_2S_2O_3$. This has a formula mass of 158 so the molecular formula is also $Na_2S_2O_3$.

Moles and concentrations of solutions

Concentration is a measure of how much solute is dissolved in a solvent.

Concentrations are measured in **moles per unit volume**. The unit of volume used may be the dm^3 or the litre. This is not as confusing as it seems because 1 dm^3 = 1 litre.

So **concentration = mol / dm^3** (sometimes written mol dm^{-3}) or **mol / litre** (sometimes written mol l^{-1}).

Concentration in mol / litre is sometimes known as **molarity** (written as M).

It is important to remember that:

$1\ dm^3\ =\ 1000\ cm^3\ =\ 1\ litre\ =\ 1000\ ml$ which means that

concentration = mol / dm^3 = mol × 1000 / volume in cm^3

To calculate the amount of solute in solution, you need to know both the concentration and volume of the solution.

MASS AND VOLUME TO CONCENTRATION
Process
1. Calculate moles of solute
2. Scale volume to 1 dm^3

WORKED EXAMPLES
5.85 g of sodium chloride is dissolved in 200 cm^3 of water. Calculate the concentration in mol / dm^3.

5.85 g of sodium chloride is 5.85 / (23 + 35.5) = 0.1 mol

so logically:

0.1 in 200 $\dfrac{0.1}{200}$ in 1 $\dfrac{0.1 \times 1000}{200}$ in 1000

so concentration is 0.5 mol / dm^3

or using the equation:

$$\text{concentration} = \frac{\text{mol} \times 1000}{\text{volume in } cm^3} = \frac{0.1 \times 1000}{200} = 0.5\ \text{mol} / dm^3$$

8 g of sodium hydroxide are dissolved to make 2500 cm^3 of solution. What is the concentration?

8 g of sodium hydroxide is 8 / (23 + 16 + 1) = 0.2 mol

so logically:

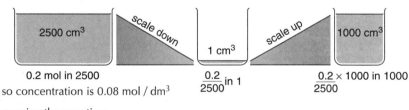

0.2 mol in 2500 $\dfrac{0.2}{2500}$ in 1 $\dfrac{0.2 \times 1000}{2500}$ in 1000

so concentration is 0.08 mol / dm^3

or using the equation:

$$\text{concentration} = \frac{\text{mol} \times 1000}{\text{volume in } cm^3} = \frac{0.2 \times 1000}{2500} = 0.08\ \text{mol} / dm^3$$

CONCENTRATION AND VOLUME TO MASS
Process
1. Write down the number of moles in 1 dm^3
2. Scale moles to the volume in the question
3. Convert from moles to mass

WORKED EXAMPLE
What mass of ammonium chloride is dissolved in 250 cm^3 of a 0.1 molar (0.1 mol / dm^3) solution?

In 1 dm^3 there is 0.1 mol

so logically:

0.1 in 1000 $\dfrac{0.1}{1000}$ in 1 $\dfrac{0.1 \times 250}{1000}$ in 250 cm^3

1 mole has a mass of (14 + 4 + 35.5) = 53.5 g

0.0250 mole has mass 0.0250 × 53.5 = 1.34 g

Moles and volumes of gases

MOLAR VOLUME
Experiments show that **1 mole of any gas has a volume of 24 dm³** (24 000 cm³) **at room temperature and atmospheric pressure** (r.t.p.).

This is an application of **Avogadro's Law** which states that **equal volumes of gases under the same conditions contain equal numbers of particles**.

At **standard temperature and pressure** (s.t.p.) 1 mole of a gas has a volume of 22.4 dm³.

half the volume
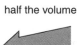
so half as many molecules of this gas

same volume

so equal numbers of molecules of each gas

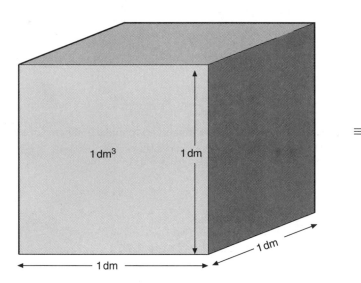

1 dm³   1 dm

1 dm

1 dm

$\equiv$ 1000 ×   1 cm   1 cm³
1 cm   1 cm

CHANGING VOLUMES TO MOLES
Key relationship

$$\frac{\text{Volume of the gas in dm}^3}{24} = \text{number of moles of the gas}$$

$$\frac{\text{Volume of gas in cm}^3}{24\,000} = \text{number of moles of the gas}$$

WORKED EXAMPLES
How many moles are there in 0.08 dm³ of hydrogen at r.t.p.?
0.08/24 = 0.00333 mol

How many moles in 125 cm³ of hydrogen chloride at r.t.p.?
125/24 000 = 0.00521 mol

CHANGING MOLES TO VOLUMES
Key relationship

Number of moles × 24 = volume of gas in dm³

Number of moles × 24 000 = volume of gas in cm³

WORKED EXAMPLES
What is the volume of 1.5 moles of air at r.t.p.?
1.5 × 24 = 36 dm³

What is the volume of 0.05 moles of chlorine at r.t.p.?
0.05 × 24 000 = 1200 cm³ or 1.2 dm³

Calculations from equations 1

In a **balanced equation** the mass of the reactants always equals the mass of the products. The equation shows matter being rearranged. Matter cannot be destroyed, so the mass of the products must be the same as the mass of the reactants.

An equation can be interpreted in two ways. For example, the equation:
$$2H_2(g) + O_2(g) \rightarrow 2H_2O(l)$$

- can be seen as representing the particles which take part in the reaction:
  2 hydrogen molecules react with **1 oxygen molecule** to make **2 water molecules**

- or can be seen as relating the number of moles which have reacted:
  2 moles of hydrogen react with **1 mole** of oxygen to make **2 moles** of water.

Of course one equation is just a scaled up version of the other, the scale factor being the Avogadro number.

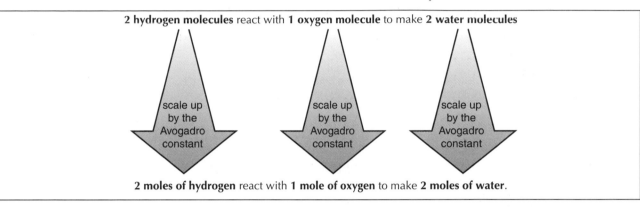

2 hydrogen molecules react with **1 oxygen molecule** to make **2 water molecules**

scale up by the Avogadro constant

scale up by the Avogadro constant

scale up by the Avogadro constant

2 moles of hydrogen react with **1 mole of oxygen** to make **2 moles of water**.

In the laboratory we think of equations in terms of moles, because we can turn moles into masses of solids (which we can weigh out) or into volumes of gases (which we can measure with a gas syringe).

So equations can be used to calculate reacting quantities.

PROCESS
1. Write out the balanced equation
2. Write out the mole ratios
3. Work out the moles of the known or given substance
4. Rewrite the mole ratio using the molar amount found in 3 above
5. Work out the moles of the unknown or wanted substance

MASS/MASS CALCULATIONS
e.g. What mass of sulphur reacts with 1.12 g of iron to make iron(II) sulphide?

1. Balanced equation

$$Fe(s) + S(s) \rightarrow FeS(s)$$

2. Mole ratios

1 mol of Fe   1 mol of S   1 mol of FeS

3. Number of moles of known substance

1.12 g of iron is 1.12/56 = 0.02 moles of iron
(remember that $\dfrac{\text{mass (g)}}{\text{formula mass}}$ = number of moles)

4. Mole ratios

0.02 mol of Fe   0.02 mol of S   0.02 mol of FeS

5. How much unknown substance

0.02 mol of sulphur = 0.02 × 32 = 0.62 g of sulphur

Calculations from equations 2

MASS/MASS CALCULATIONS
e.g. What mass of aluminium powder will burn in 1.6 g of oxygen?

1. Balanced equation

$$4Al(s) \quad + \quad 3O_2(g) \quad \rightarrow \quad 2Al_2O_3(s)$$

2. Mole ratios

4 mol of Al　　　3 mol of O_2　　　2 mol of Al_2O_3

3. Number of moles of known substance

1.6 g of oxygen is $\dfrac{1.6}{32}$ = 0.05 mol

(remember that $\dfrac{\text{mass (g)}}{\text{formula mass}}$ = number of moles)

4. Mole ratios

From step 2:

	4 mol	3 mol	2 mol
so	4/3 mol	1 mol	2/3 mol
so	4/3 × 0.05 mol	0.05 mol	2/3 × 0.05 mol

5. How much unknown substance

4/3 × 0.05 mol of aluminium is 0.067 mol. This has a mass of 0.067 × 27 = 1.8 g.

MASS/VOLUME CALCULATIONS
e.g. What volume of ammonia reacts with 4 g of copper oxide?

1. Balanced equation

$$3CuO(s) \quad + \quad 2NH_3(g) \quad \rightarrow \quad 3Cu(s) \quad + \quad 3H_2O(g) \quad + \quad N_2(g)$$

2. Mole ratios

3 mol of CuO　　2 mol of NH_3　　3 mol of Cu　　3 mol of H_2O　　1 mol of N_2

3. Number of moles of known substance

4 g of copper oxide is $\dfrac{4}{(64 + 16)}$ = 0.05 mol

(remember that $\dfrac{\text{mass (g)}}{\text{formula mass}}$ = number of moles)

4. Mole ratios

Step 2 gave

	3 mol	2 mol	3 mol	3 mol	1 mol
so	1 mol	2/3 mol	1 mol	1 mol	1/3 mol
so	0.05 mol	2/3 × 0.05 mol	0.05 mol	0.05 mol	1/3 × 0.05 mol

5. How much unknown substance

2/3 × 0.05 mol of ammonia has a volume of 2/3 × 0.05 × 24000 = 800 cm³

VOLUME/VOLUME CALCULATIONS FOR GASES
e.g. What volume of oxygen is needed for the complete combustion of 50 cm³ of propane, C_3H_8?

1. Balanced equation

$$C_3H_8(g) \quad + \quad 5O_2(g) \quad \rightarrow \quad 3CO_2(g) \quad + \quad 4H_2O(g)$$

2. Mole ratios

1 mol of C_3H_8　　5 mol of O_2　　3 mol of CO_2　　4 mol of H_2O

3. Now remember Avogadro's law. Equal volumes of gases contain equal numbers of particles. That means that equal numbers of molecules occupy equal volumes. So we can simply convert from a mole ratio to a volume ratio.

　　　1 volume　　　5 volumes　　　3 volumes　　　4 volumes

and so 50 cm³ of C_3H_8　5 × 50 cm³ of O_2　3 × 50 cm³ of CO_2　4 × 50 cm³ of H_2O

so the volume of oxygen needed is 250 cm³.

Calculations from equations 3

MASS/VOLUME CALCULATIONS FOR SOLUTIONS
e.g. What volume of 2 mol / dm³ sulphuric acid is needed to react with 3 g of magnesium?

1. Balanced equation

$$Mg(s) \quad + \quad H_2SO_4(aq) \quad \rightarrow \quad MgSO_4(aq) \quad + \quad H_2(g)$$

2. Mole ratios

1 mol of Mg   1 mol of H_2SO_4 1 mol of $MgSO_4$ 1 mol of H_2

3. Number of moles of known substance

3 g of magnesium is 3/24 = 0.125 mol

(remember that $\dfrac{\text{mass (g)}}{\text{formula mass}}$ = number of moles)

4. Mole ratios

0.125 mol   0.125 mol   0.125 mol   0.125 mol

5. How much unknown substance

2 mol in 1000 cm³   scale down ratio of 2:1   1 mol in $\frac{1}{2}\times 1000$ scale down ratio of 1:0.125   0.125 mol in $0.125 \times \frac{1}{2} \times 1000$ = **62.5 cm³**

VOLUME/VOLUME CALCULATIONS FOR SOLUTIONS (USED IN TITRATIONS)
e.g. What volume of 0.15 mol / dm³ sodium carbonate solution is needed to neutralize 20 cm³ of 0.1 mol / dm³ hydrochloric acid?

1. Balanced equation

$$2HCl(aq) \quad + \quad Na_2CO_3(aq) \quad \rightarrow \quad 2NaCl(aq) \quad + \quad H_2O(l) \quad + \quad CO_2(g)$$

2. Mole ratios

2 mol of HCl   1 mol of Na_2CO_3 2 mol of NaCl   1 mol of H_2O 1 mol of CO_2

3. Number of moles of known substance

1000 cm³ contain 0.1 mol   scale down to 1   1 cm³ contains $\frac{1}{1000}\times 0.1$ scale up to 20   20 cm³ contains $20 \times \frac{1}{1000} \times 0.1$ = **0.002 mol**

4. Mole ratios

0.002 mol   0.001 mol   0.002 mol   0.001 mol   0.001 mol

5. How much unknown substance

0.15 mol in 1000 cm³   scale up $\frac{0.15}{0.15}$ scale up   similarly   1 mol in $\frac{1000}{0.15}$ 1 × 0.001 scale down   similarly   0.001 mol in $0.001 \times \frac{1000}{0.15}$ = **6.67 cm³**

SAMPLE TITRATION CALCULATION
20 cm³ of sodium hydroxide was pipetted into a conical flask and titrated against 0.10 mol / dm³ sulphuric acid using methyl orange as indicator. The indicator changed colour when 15.6 cm³ of acid had been added from the burette. Calculate the concentration of the sodium hydroxide solution.

1. Balanced equation

$$H_2SO_4(aq) \quad + \quad 2NaOH(aq) \quad \rightarrow \quad Na_2SO_4(aq) \quad + \quad 2H_2O(l)$$

2. Mole ratios

1 mol of H_2SO_4 2 mol of NaOH   1 mol of Na_2SO_4 2 mol of H_2O

3. Number of moles of known substance

1000 cm³ contain 0.1 mol   scale down   1 cm³ contains $\frac{1}{1000}\times 0.1$ scale up   15.6 cm³ contains $15.6 \times \frac{1}{1000} \times 0.1$ = **0.00156 mol**

4. Mole ratios

0.00156 mol   2 × 0.00156 mol   0.00156 mol   2 × 0.00156 mol

5. How much unknown substance

20 cm³ contain 2 × 0.00156 mol   scale down   1 cm³ contains $\frac{1}{20} \times 2 \times 0.00156$ mol   scale up   1000 cm³ contains $1000 \times \frac{1}{20} \times 2 \times 0.00156$ = **0.156 mol/dm³**

Electrolysis calculations

Electrons coming from anode

Anions lose electrons.
Anode reactions are oxidations.

Electrons going to the cathode

Cations gain electrons.
Cathode reactions are reductions.

ELECTROLYSIS
In electrolysis electrons are lost and gained by ions at the electrodes. These electrons are pumped round the circuit by a battery or power pack.

The amount of electrolysis depends on the number of electrons which flow round the circuit, i.e. the amount of **charge**. Charge is measured in **coulombs**. The relationship between current, time, and charge is:

amps × seconds = coulombs

The charge carried by **1 mole of electrons** is called the **Faraday**.

1 Faraday is 96 500 coulombs.

The mass of substance discharged at an electrode depends on:

• **the current flowing**
• **the time the current flows for**
• **the charge on the ion**
  Ions with a double charge need twice as many electrons to discharge them as ions with a single charge.
  $Ca^{2+} + 2e^- \rightarrow Ca$ compared with $Na^+ + 1e^- \rightarrow Na$

ELECTROLYSIS CALCULATIONS
Follow the same five steps as in other calculations from equations.

e.g. A current of 12 amps flows through molten lead bromide for 15 minutes. Calculate the masses of lead and bromine produced at the electrodes.

1. Balanced equations

Anode: $2Br^-(l) \rightarrow Br_2(g) + 2e^-$ **Cathode**: $Pb^{2+}(l) + 2e^- \rightarrow Pb(l)$

2. Mole ratios

2 mol 1 mol 2 mol 1 mol 2 mol 1 mol

3. Number of moles of electrons

charge = 12 × 15 × 60 (current × time *in seconds*)
       = 10 800 coulombs
which is 10 800/96 500 = 0.112 mol of electrons (Faraday)

4. Mole ratios

0.112 0.5 × 0.112 0.112 0.5 × 0.112 0.112 0.5 × 0.112

5. How much unknown substance

0.5 x 0.112 mol of bromine = 0.5 x 0.112 x 79 x 2 = 8.84 g of bromine
0.5 x 0.112 mol of lead = 0.5 x 0.112 x 208 = 11.6 g of lead

e.g. A current of 100 000 amps is passed through the Hall cell in an aluminium plant for 1 hour. What mass of aluminium is deposited and what volume of oxygen is produced?

1. Balanced equations

Anode: $2O^{2-}(l) \rightarrow O_2(g) + 4e^-$ **Cathode**: $Al^{3+}(l) + 3e^- \rightarrow Al(l)$

2. Mole ratios

2 mol 1 mol 4 mol 1 mol 3 mol 1 mol

3. Number of moles of electrons

charge = 100 000 x 60 x 60 (current x time in seconds)
       = 360 000 000 coulombs
which is 360 000 000/96 500 = 3730 mol of electrons

4. Mole ratios

1/2 × 3730 1/4 × 3730 3730 1/3 × 3730 3730 1/3 × 3730

5. How much unknown substance

1/4 x 3730 mol of oxygen = 1/4 × 3730 × 24 dm³
                        = 21 500 dm³
1/3 x 3730 mol of aluminium = 1/3 × 3730 × 27 g
                           = 33 200 g
                           = 33.2 kg

Making salts in the laboratory

SOLUBILITY RULES FOR SALTS
- all Group 1 compounds are soluble
- all nitrates are soluble
- all chlorides are soluble except silver and lead
- all sulphates are soluble except calcium, barium, and lead
- all carbonates are insoluble except Group 1

SOLUBILITY RULES FOR BASES
- all Group 1 bases are soluble
- in Group 2, calcium and barium salts are soluble
- ammonia is soluble

DECIDE IF THE SALT IS SOLUBLE USING SOLUBILITY RULES

Salt is soluble →

Salt is insoluble →

USE TITRATION

1. Measure out a volume of alkaline solution, say 20 cm³. Add some phenolphthalein indicator, then run acid into the flask from a burette.
2. Continue adding acid until one more drop of acid is just enough to turn the solution from pink to colourless. The base has now been neutralized.
3. Note the volume of acid needed for the neutralization (this is the reading on the burette).
4. Repeat the process, this time without adding indicator. Run the measured volume of acid from the burette into the 20 cm³ of alkali in the flask.
5. Evaporate off most of the water from the solution over a water bath. Leave the remaining solution to cool, so that the salt can crystallize out. Dry off the crystals on filter paper.

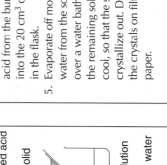

Burette
Acid
Alkali
Start
Finish
21
22
0
1
Salt solution
Boiling water
Heat

MAKE THE SALT BY NEUTRALIZATION
- Choose the appropriate acid, e.g. HCl for chlorides, HNO₃ for nitrates, H₂SO₄ for sulphates
- add either
  (a) a reactive metal: Mg, Al, Fe, Zn
  or (b) a base: a metal oxide, hydroxide, or carbonate
- if you are adding a base, decide whether it is soluble

If you are adding a soluble base →

If you are adding a metal or insoluble base →

USE EXCESS BASE METHOD

1. Measure out a volume of acid solution. Add a spatula full of solid: metal, metal oxide, metal hydroxide, or metal carbonate. Warm the beaker.
2. Continue adding solid reactant to the solution until no more dissolves. Warm and stir the solution to make sure the reaction is complete.
3. Filter off the excess solid and collect the filtrate, which is a pure salt solution.
4. Evaporate off most of the water from the solution over a warm bath. Leave the remaining solution to cool, so that the salt can crystallize out. Dry off the crystals on filter paper.

Base
Acid solution
Heat
Neutralized acid
Excess solid
Heat
Pure salt solution
Salt solution
Boiling water
Heat

MAKE THE SALT BY PRECIPITATION
Use the solubility rules to think of two solutions, one having the cation, the other the anion.

1. Add the cation solution to the anion solution.
2. Filter the resulting suspension.
3. Wash then dry the residue.

Cation solution
Precipitate of the insoluble salt forming in anion solution
Suspension of insoluble salt
Insoluble salt forms residue

Measuring solubility

It is easier to see the first crystals forming as a saturated solution cools than it is to judge when the very last crystal dissolves as the solution is heated. So to measure solubility, you cool solutions of different concentrations and record the temperature when the first crystals appear on the surface (the coolest part of the solution) and then sink to the bottom. If you miss this moment, you can always reheat the solution and repeat the reading.

The different solutions are made by adding more and more water to the same mass of solute.

SAFETY!
- follow instructions precisely
- wear safety glasses
- take care with hot objects
- wipe up any spilled substances

PROCEDURE FOR POTASSIUM NITRATE

1. Weigh a boiling tube.

2. Add about 12 g of potassium nitrate, and re-weigh.

3. Add 10 cm³ (10 g) of water from a burette.

   Burette
   Water

6. Record the temperature at which crystals first appear and sink.

   — T °C

5. Clamp a thermometer so that it hangs in the middle of the tube.

4. Heat until all the crystals of potassium nitrate have dissolved.

7. Add 2 cm³ (2 g) more water to the solution in the tube.

8. Repeat steps 4, 5, and 6.

9. Repeat steps 7 and 8 until 20 cm³ (20 g) water in all have been added.

11. Plot the results to give a solubility curve.

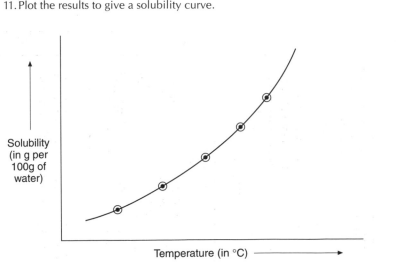

Solubility (in g per 100g of water)

Temperature (in °C)

10. Tabulate readings and calculate solubility in g / 100 g for each temperature.

Titrations

In a titration you react a known volume of one solution (measured in a **pipette**) with a known volume of another solution (measured in a **burette**). You can tell when the reaction is complete because

- *either* an indicator which has been added changes colour, *or*
- one of the solutions itself changes colour.

SAFETY!
- follow instructions precisely
- wear safety glasses
- acids and alkalis are corrosive: handle them carefully and mop up any spills

PROCEDURE

1. Label and fill two beakers with the reacting solutions.

ACID   ALKALI

2. Pour a little of one solution into the burette to rinse it. Check the tap works. Pour away all this solution.

3. Fill the burette. Run liquid through the tap until there are no air bubbles. Zero the burette.

4. Using a pipette filler, rinse out the pipette with the other solution. Then refill the pipette to well above the mark.

pipette filler

5. Carefully let the solution out until the meniscus is on the line.

6. Run this solution into a conical flask. Do not force out the last drop, but just touch the pipette tip on the liquid surface.

7. Add just enough indicator to produce a definite colour (about 2–5 drops). Put the conical flask on a white tile. Adjust the height of the burette so that it just sticks into the neck of the conical flask.

8. Run solution from the burette into the conical flask, swirling the flask all the time. Do not shake the flask, or solution will get splashed up the sides where it may not react.

9. Stop when the indicator changes colour and note the volume run in from the burette.

10. Empty and rinse the conical flask. It need not be dried, because any water will dilute both solutions equally.

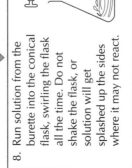

11. Refill and re-zero the burette.

12. Using the pipette filler, refill the pipette and zero it.

13. Repeat steps 5, 6, and 7.

14. Repeat step 8 but this time stop about 1 cm³ before the previously recorded volume. Then add the solution drop by drop until the colour just changes.

15. Record the volume added in a table

Final reading ———
Initial reading ———
Volume added ———

16. Do at least two accurate titrations and work out the average volume added.

Testing for cations

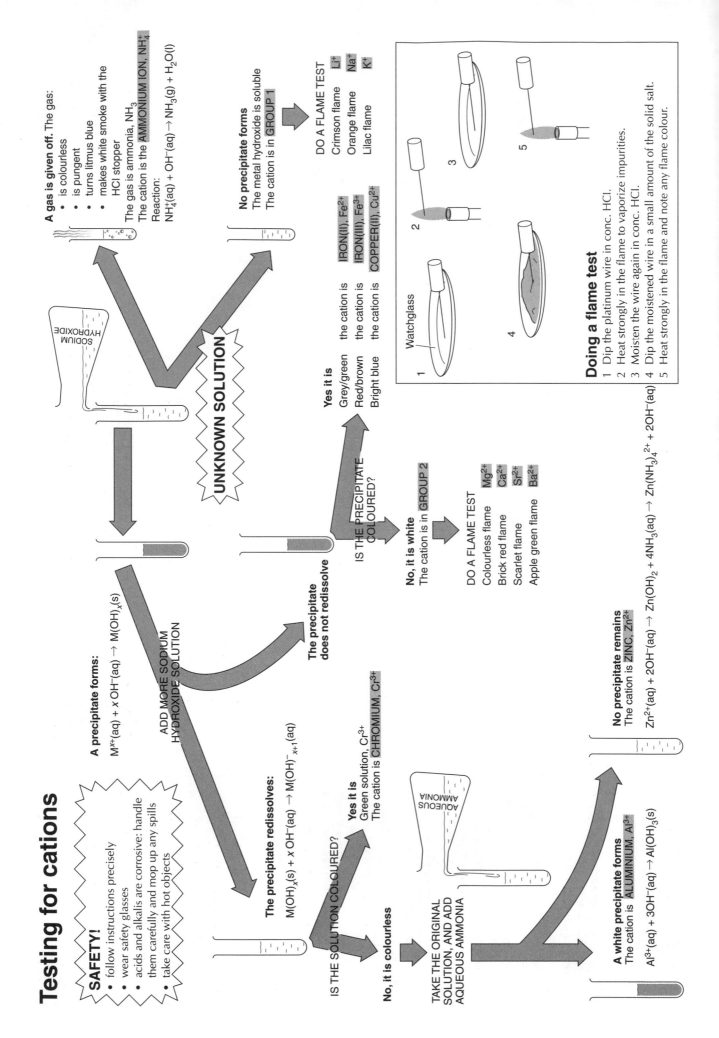

SAFETY!
- follow instructions precisely
- wear safety glasses
- acids and alkalis are corrosive: handle them carefully and mop up any spills
- take care with hot objects

UNKNOWN SOLUTION

A precipitate forms:
$M^{x+}(aq) + x\ OH^-(aq) \rightarrow M(OH)_x(s)$

ADD MORE SODIUM HYDROXIDE SOLUTION

SODIUM HYDROXIDE

A gas is given off. The gas:
- is colourless
- is pungent
- turns litmus blue
- makes white smoke with the HCl stopper

The gas is ammonia, NH_3
The cation is the AMMONIUM ION, NH_4^+
Reaction:
$NH_4^+(aq) + OH^-(aq) \rightarrow NH_3(g) + H_2O(l)$

No precipitate forms
The metal hydroxide is soluble
The cation is in GROUP 1

DO A FLAME TEST
Crimson flame   Li⁺ — Li^+
Orange flame   Na⁺ — Na^+
Lilac flame   K⁺ — K^+

The precipitate redissolves:
$M(OH)_x(s) + x\ OH^-(aq) \rightarrow M(OH)^-_{x+1}(aq)$

IS THE SOLUTION COLOURED?

Yes it is
Green solution, Cr^{3+}
The cation is CHROMIUM, Cr^{3+}

No, it is colourless

TAKE THE ORIGINAL SOLUTION, AND ADD AQUEOUS AMMONIA

AQUEOUS AMMONIA

A white precipitate forms
The cation is ALUMINIUM, Al^{3+}
$Al^{3+}(aq) + 3OH^-(aq) \rightarrow Al(OH)_3(s)$

No precipitate remains
The cation is ZINC, Zn^{2+}
$Zn^{2+}(aq) + 2OH^-(aq) \rightarrow Zn(OH)_2 + 4NH_3(aq) \rightarrow Zn(NH_3)_4{}^{2+} + 2OH^-(aq)$

The precipitate does not redissolve

IS THE PRECIPITATE COLOURED?

Yes it is
Grey/green   the cation is   IRON(II), Fe^{2+}
Red/brown   the cation is   IRON(III), Fe^{3+}
Bright blue the cation is   COPPER(II), Cu^{2+}

No, it is white
The cation is in GROUP 2

DO A FLAME TEST
Colourless flame   Mg²⁺ — Mg^{2+}
Brick red flame   Ca²⁺ — Ca^{2+}
Scarlet flame   Sr²⁺ — Sr^{2+}
Apple green flame   Ba²⁺ — Ba^{2+}

Doing a flame test
1 Dip the platinum wire in conc. HCl.
2 Heat strongly in the flame to vaporize impurities.
3 Moisten the wire again in conc. HCl.
4 Dip the moistened wire in a small amount of the solid salt.
5 Heat strongly in the flame and note any flame colour.

Watchglass

Testing for anions

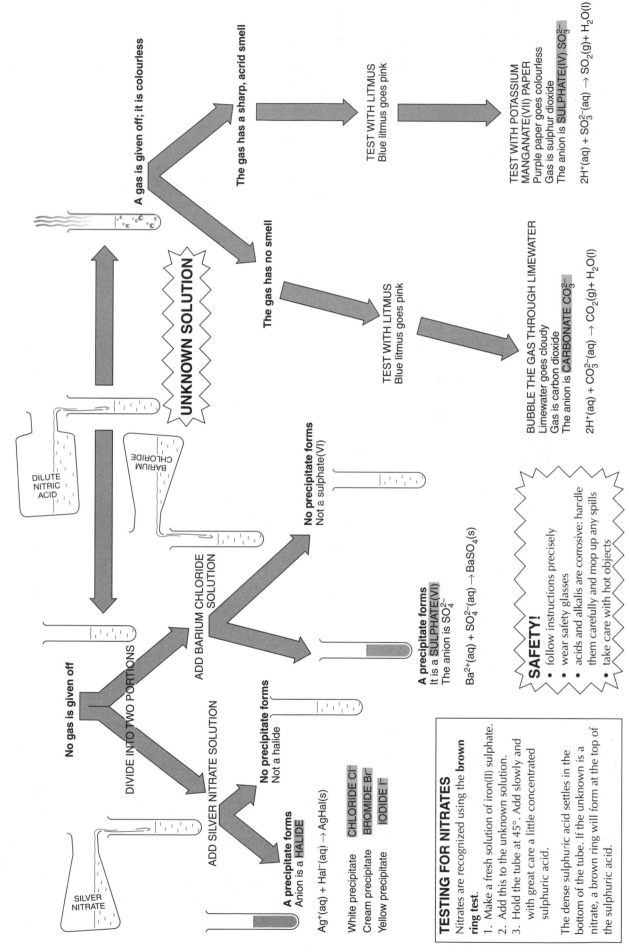

A gas is given off; it is colourless

The gas has a sharp, acrid smell

TEST WITH LITMUS
Blue litmus goes pink

TEST WITH POTASSIUM
MANGANATE(VII) PAPER
Purple paper goes colourless
Gas is sulphur dioxide
The anion is SULPHATE(IV) SO_3^{2-}

$2H^+(aq) + SO_3^{2-}(aq) \rightarrow SO_2(g) + H_2O(l)$

The gas has no smell

TEST WITH LITMUS
Blue litmus goes pink

BUBBLE THE GAS THROUGH LIMEWATER
Limewater goes cloudy
Gas is carbon dioxide
The anion is CARBONATE CO_3^{2-}

$2H^+(aq) + CO_3^{2-}(aq) \rightarrow CO_2(g) + H_2O(l)$

UNKNOWN SOLUTION

DILUTE
NITRIC
ACID

BARIUM
CHLORIDE

No gas is given off

DIVIDE INTO TWO PORTIONS

ADD BARIUM CHLORIDE
SOLUTION

No precipitate forms
Not a sulphate(VI)

A precipitate forms
It is a SULPHATE(VI)
The anion is SO_4^{2-}

$Ba^{2+}(aq) + SO_4^{2-}(aq) \rightarrow BaSO_4(s)$

ADD SILVER NITRATE SOLUTION

No precipitate forms
Not a halide

A precipitate forms
Anion is a HALIDE

$Ag^+(aq) + Hal^-(aq) \rightarrow AgHal(s)$

White precipitate   CHLORIDE Cl⁻
Cream precipitate   BROMIDE Br⁻
Yellow precipitate   IODIDE I⁻

SILVER
NITRATE

TESTING FOR NITRATES

Nitrates are recognized using the **brown ring test.**

1. Make a fresh solution of iron(II) sulphate.
2. Add this to the unknown solution.
3. Hold the tube at 45°. Add slowly and with great care a little concentrated sulphuric acid.

The dense sulphuric acid settles in the bottom of the tube. If the unknown is a nitrate, a brown ring will form at the top of the sulphuric acid.

SAFETY!

- follow instructions precisely
- wear safety glasses
- acids and alkalis are corrosive: handle them carefully and mop up any spills
- take care with hot objects

Making and testing for gases in the laboratory

MAKING GASES
Gases are always made from the reaction between a solid and a liquid. The volume of gas made is controlled by the amount of liquid run into the flask holding the solid reactant.

Gas	Liquid	Solid	Reaction
Hydrogen	Dilute sulphuric acid	Magnesium	$H_2SO_4 + Mg \rightarrow H_2 + MgSO_4$
Oxygen	Hydrogen peroxide	Manganese(IV) oxide	$2H_2O_2 \rightarrow O_2 + 2H_2O$
Carbon dioxide	Dilute hydrochloric acid	Calcium carbonate	$2HCl + CaCO_3 \rightarrow CO_2 + CaCl_2 + H_2O$
Hydrogen chloride	Conc. sulphuric acid	Sodium chloride	$H_2SO_4 + 2NaCl \rightarrow 2HCl + Na_2SO_4$
Ammonia	Sodium hydroxide	Ammonium chloride	$NaOH + NH_4Cl \rightarrow NH_3 + NaCl + H_2O$
Sulphur dioxide	Dilute hydrochloric acid	Sodium sulphate(IV)	$2HCl + Na_2SO_3 \rightarrow SO_2 + 2NaCl + H_2O$
Chlorine	Conc. hydrochloric acid	Manganese(IV) oxide	$4HCl + MnO_2 \rightarrow Cl_2 + MnCl_2 + 2H_2O$
Nitrogen dioxide	Dilute nitric acid	Copper metal	$4HNO_3 + Cu \rightarrow Cu(NO_3)_2 + 2NO_2 + H_2O$

Drying gases
Because the liquid involved in the reaction is often an aqueous solution, the gas produced is often wet (contaminated with water).

Gases can be dried by passing them through something which reacts with (and so removes) the water.

Acidic and neutral gases are dried by passing them through concentrated sulphuric acid.

Ammonia is an alkaline gas. It is dried by passing it over calcium chloride granules.

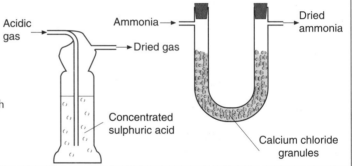

TESTING FOR GASES IN THE LAB

1. Look at its colour
Most gases are colourless but chlorine is green and nitrogen dioxide is brown.

2. Cautiously smell the gas
- Many gases have no smell: oxygen, hydrogen, nitrogen, carbon dioxide.
- Some smell acrid (this means a sharp smell which makes you jerk your head back): sulphur dioxide, hydrogen chloride.
- Others are pungent (they have a very strong smell): ammonia.
- Others have a characteristic or familiar smell: chlorine has a smell we all know from swimming pools.

3. Test with damp litmus paper
Remember that the only positive test is one in which the paper changes colour.
- Litmus goes pink (acidic): hydrogen chloride, sulphur dioxide, carbon dioxide.
- Litmus goes blue (alkaline): ammonia.

Indicator paper folded down the middle and wetted

4. Then confirm the identity of the gas with a special test
hydrogen	ignites with a squeaky pop
oxygen	relights a glowing splint
carbon dioxide	turns calcium hydroxide (lime water) cloudy
hydrogen chloride	white smoke forms with the ammonia bottle stopper
ammonia	white smoke forms with the concentrated hydrochloric acid bottle stopper
sulphur dioxide	potassium manganate(VII) on filter paper goes colourless
chlorine	potassium iodide on filter paper goes brown
nitrogen dioxide	a piece of copper goes green

Sample exam question answers

On the following pages some sample examination questions are answered. As you study them try to notice the following key points:

- what are you told to do and has the answer done it? key words to look for are: *list; describe; explain; suggest; predict*
- the number of marks offered must be matched by the number of points made
- can you recognise what part of the syllabus is covered by the question because this will guide you to the likely answer
- many of these questions contain hints or even the information you need to answer the question, so study the question very carefully before and while you are answering it

(MEG bear no responsibility for the answers provided.)

1 Complete this table about metals, their uses and the properties which make them suitable for these uses.

The first line has been completed for you.

metal	use	property which makes the metal suitable for this use
aluminium	aeroplane body	low density
copper	saucepan base	conductivity
lead	church roof	malleable
mercury	thermometer	liquid at room temperature
gold	jewellery	shiny appearance
steel	bridges	strong
tin	coating food cans	unreactive
tungsten	lamp filament	high melting point

(7)

(MEG)

Here you must use your general knowledge as well as what you have learnt in chemistry

What do you want a good saucepan to do? It must let the heat from the cooker through easily

What is needed for a roofing material? Something which can spread over the roof matching its shape

This question is easy and obvious

So is this one

You might have to guess here. What other reasons are there for coating a can? You might well get a mark for this too

Make sure here that you give a use which depends on strength

What is the most obvious thing about the filament in a lamp? It is white hot. Why doesn't it melt?

8 This question is about the use of different materials in the home

The table gives information about the properties of some materials.

material	melting point below 500°C	melting point above 500°C	density	thermal conductivity	bulk properties	
ceramic		yes	medium	low	hard	brittle
glass		yes	medium	low	hard	brittle
iron		yes	(high)	(high)	hard	(malleable)
thermoplastic	yes		low	low	soft	elastic
thermoset plastic		yes	low	low	hard	brittle

Use the information in the table to answer the following questions.

(a) Both ceramics and iron are used to make cooking pots.

   (i) Describe one advantage of using iron rather than ceramics for cooking pots.

> *They are not brittle. They do not break when dropped or banged against something else.*
>
> (1)

   (ii) Describe one advantage of using ceramics rather than iron for cooking pots.

> *They are not as heavy. Their density is medium. Iron's is high.*
>
> (1)

(b) Glass and iron have different properties caused by their different arrangement of atoms.

   (i) Describe a difference in the arrangement of atoms in glass and iron

> *The atoms in glass are randomly arranged, those in iron are in a regular lattice.*
>
> (2)

   (ii) How does the arrangement of atoms help to explain why glass is brittle but iron is malleable?

> *In glass there are no layers of atoms which can slide over each other as they do in iron, so in glass moving the atoms makes it break.*
>
> (2)

(c) The properties of iron can be altered by adding another metal to make an alloy

   (i) Suggest a property of iron that could be changed by adding another metal.

> *Hardness*
>
> (1)

   (ii) Explain in terms of atoms, how the addition of another metal to iron causes this change.

> *Atoms of a different size stop the layers of iron atoms sliding over each other.*
>
> (2)

(MEG)

Look at the table and find the columns where iron is different from all the others. The conductivity is another perfectly correct answer instead of malleability

You are looking for an advantage so you cannot use conductivity. Apart from the two mentioned above, density is the only other property in which iron differs from a ceramic

For two marks, try to say something about both the glass and iron lattices.

Malleability is a key metallic property and is caused by layers of atoms sliding past each other. If glass is not malleable, then the atoms in it cannot slide past each other.

Make sure you choose a property you can explain in part (ii).

(d) Thermoset plastics are often used to make the bodies of electric kettles.

    (i) What advantage does this use of thermoset plastics have over the use of iron?

        They are poor conductors of heat. They will not feel so hot.

        (1)

    (ii) What advantage does this use of thermoset plastics have over the use of thermoplastics?

        They do not soften when they are heated.

        (1)

    (iii) Explain the difference in properties of thermoplastics and thermosets in terms of their structures.

        Thermoplastics soften when heated because they have weak (Van der Waals) forces between the chains of atoms. Thermosets have strong covalent cross-links between the chains. Heat energy breaks the weak forces but not the strong ones.

        (3)

        (MEG)

10 Indigestion tablets contain substances which neutralise excess hydrochloric acid in the stomach.

The labels from two makes of tablets are shown

INDICALM	**Stomachease**
Indigestion tablets	*for fast indigestion relief*
each tablet contains 250mg of calcium carbonate	each tablet contains 250mg of magnesium hydroxide

(a) (i) Balance this equation for the reaction between calcium carbonate and hydrochloric acid.

$$CaCO_3 + HCl = CaCl_2 + CO_2 + H_2O$$

$$\underline{CaCO_3 + 2\,HCl = CaCl_2 + CO_2 + H_2O}$$

(2)

On the right-hand side there are two chlorines and two hydrogens, so there must be two HCls on the left-handside

(ii) Write a balanced equation for the reaction between magnesium hydroxide, $Mg(OH)_2$ and hydrochloric acid, HCl.

$$\underline{Mg(OH)_2 + 2\,HCl = MgCl_2 + 2H_2O}$$

(2)

Magnesium is in the same group as calcium, so the formula of magnesium chloride will be similar to that of calcium chloride. The other product from acid + base must be water. Now balance the atoms systematically

(b) The stomach contains hydrochloric acid of concentration 1.0 mol/dm^3.

Find by calculation which indigestion tablet will neutralise the larger volume of this acid.

You must show your working.

Relative Atomic Masses: Ca = 40; Mg = 24; O = 16; C = 12.

$$\text{amount of substance (mol)} = \frac{\text{mass of substance (g)}}{\text{molar mass (g/mol)}}$$

$$\underset{\text{(mol)}}{\text{amount of substance in solution}} = \underset{\text{(litres)}}{\text{volume of solution}} \times \underset{\text{(mol/litre)}}{\text{concentration}}$$

Molar mass of calcium carbonate = 40 + 12 + 48 = 100

Amount of calcium carbonate = $\frac{0.250}{100}$ = 2.5 x 10^{-3} mol

Molar mass of magnesium hydroxide = 24 + 32 + 2 = 58

Amount of magnesium hydroxide = $\frac{0.250}{58}$ = 4.31 x 10^{-3} mol

From the equations, each base reacts with twice the amount of acid.

There is a greater amount of magnesium hyrdoxide so it will neutralise the larger amount of acid which is 2 x 4.31 x 10^{-3}
$$= 8.62 \times 10^{-3}\ \text{moles}$$

There is 1 mol in 1000cm^3
so there will be 8.62 x 10^{-3} mol in 8.62 cm^3 of acid

Use the formulas given to you and work out the amount of each base in the mass given on the labels. As in both equations, one mole of each base reacts with two moles of acid, the greater amount of base will need the greater amount of acid

(MEG)

11 The table gives information about some substances.

	boiling point °C	electrical conductivity (molten)	density g/cm³
carbon dioxide	−78	poor	0.002
diamond	4800	poor	3.500
silicon dioxide	2230	poor	2.650
sodium chloride	1413	good	2.170
sulphur dioxide	−10	poor	0.003

(a) (i) Which two substances in the table are made of simple molecules?

1. Carbon dioxide

2. Sulphur dioxide

(2)

Look at the boiling points. Two substances have low boiling points compared to the other three.

(ii) Use your knowledge of the forces between atoms and molecules to explain the difference in density of carbon dioxide and diamond.

In diamond all the atoms are covalently bonded

closely together so diamond has high density.

Carbon dioxide is made of separate molecules

weakly bonded to each other so the density is low.

(4)

To gain four marks, try to say something about the bonding and density in each substance

(b) Explain why:

(i) Solid sodium chloride will not conduct electricity, but molten sodium chloride will.

In solid sodium chloride the ions are held fixed in the

lattice. When sodium chloride melts the ions become

free to move and carry charge through the liquid.

(3)

Remember that for a substance to conduct, there must be charged particles free to move. In metals, the charged particles are the outer, delocalised electrons, but here they are ions which can only move in the liquid state

(ii) Molten silicon dioxide will not conduct electricity, but molten sodium chloride will.

Silicon dioxide is a covalent substance and contains

no ions so there is nothing to carry the charge.

(1)

(MEG)

Only one point to make here. Without any ions conduction will not happen

Self-assessment questions

1 This picture combines the water cycle with the weathering of rocks.

Add the words evaporation, condensation, erosion, transportation and deposition in suitable places. (5)

2 Here are the colours of three indicators between pH 1 and 13:

pH		
	1 2 3 4 5 6 7 8 9 10 11 12 13 14	
methyl red	red change yellow	
litmus	red change blue	
phenolphthalein	colourless change red	

Give the colours of the following mixtures. (4)
a   pure water + litmus
b   sulphuric acid + methyl red
c   sodium hydroxide (pH13) + methyl red + phenolphthalein
d   alkali + phenolphthalein

3 Lumps of calcium carbonate react with dilute nitric acid to give carbon dioxide gas and a solution of calcium nitrate. (Relative atomic masses are: Ca = 40; C = 12; O = 16; H = 14)
a   Write a balanced chemical equation for this reaction (2)
b   What mass of carbon dioxide will result from the reaction of 10g of calcium carbonate with excess nitric acid? (2)

4 Combustion is the process that happens when a fuel burns.
a   What is the fuel in a candle? (1)
b   What is the main type of energy that results from combustion? (1)
c   Name the two main waste gases produced by the combustion of petrol. (2)
d   Name the gas that reacts with the fuel during combustion. (1)

5 The following boxes contain information about the layers that make up the Earth.
a   Label each box with the correct letter:
C = crust   M = mantle
OC = outer core   IC = inner core. (4)

liquid; mainly iron; up to 4000 °C	
solid; rock; 250°C (average)	
plastic solid; rock; up to 3700°C	
solid; mainly iron; up to 4500°C	

b   Iron usually melts at 1535 °C. Explain why iron inside the Earth is solid at 4500 °C. (1)
c   Explain why scientists believe that rocks in the mantle have a higher density than rocks in the crust. (2)

6 A salt is made when an acid reacts with a metal or a metal compound. Fill in the gaps in the following table. (5)

Salt	Metal/metal compound	Acid
zinc sulphate		sulphuric acid
	lead carbonate	nitric acid
sodium chloride		
copper sulphate		sulphuric acid

7 a   Using circles to represent water molecules, draw diagrams to show the arrangement of molecules in ice (solid), water (liquid), and steam (gas). (3)
b   Why do ice cubes have a fixed shape? (1)

8 Refer to the metal reactivity series to explain why a blast furnace cannot be used to extract aluminium from its ore. (2)

9 Sodium is a metallic element; sodium chloride is a compound containing sodium; sodium chloride dissolves in water.
a   Choose from the words ions, atoms, molecules, to describe the main particles present in:
(i)   sodium
(ii)   sodium chloride
(iii) water. (2)
b   Explain why sodium chloride (m.p. 801°C) has a much higher melting point than water.
c   Explain why sodium chloride solution conducts electricity, whereas solid sodium chloride does not. (3)

10 This diagram shows an active volcano.

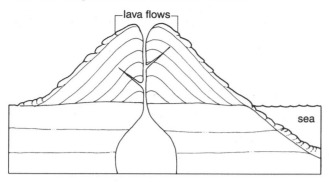

Shade and label (with letters **a b c d**) the regions where you would most likely find:
a metamorphic rock
b igneous rock with small crystals
c igneous rock with large crystals
d sedimentary rock.   (4)

11 Jack adds samples of four metals A, B, C, and D to water and to acid. He notes down the following results:

Metal	Reaction with water	Reaction with acid
A	none	slow
B	none	none
C	rapid	violent
D	very slow	rapid

a Arrange the metals in order of increasing reactivity.   (2)
b Jack dissolves the chloride salt of metal B in water and then adds metal A. Does he expect anything to happen? Explain your answer.   (2)

12 Changes happen at the electrodes during electrolysis. Fill in the chart to show what you expect to happen.   (4)

Electrolysis system	At the anode(+)	At the cathode (−)
copper sulphate between copper electrodes		
dilute sulphuric acid between carbon electrodes		

13 Rusting is the corrosion of iron and many of its alloys.
a What two substances must be present for rusting to happen?   (2)
b Roman swords made of iron have been found in peat bogs. Why have these swords not completely rusted away?   (1)
c What do rusting and combustion have in common?   (1)

14 Seranjit has four different powders in bottles whose labels have fallen off. She tests each powder by adding a little to some dilute hydrochloric acid. These are the results she wrote down:

Bottle 1
All dissolved: hydrogen given off

Bottle 2
Nothing happened

Bottle 3
All dissolved: CO_2 given off

Bottle 4
Some dissolved, but not all

On which bottle should Seranjit stick each of the following labels?   (4)

MAGNESIUM

SILICON

MAGNESIUM/SILICON MIXTURE

MAGNESIUM CARBONATE

15 The table contains information about the five elements A–E (not their actual symbols).

Element	Group number	Proton number	Nucleon number
A	I	11	23
B	II	20	40
C	VI	16	32
D	0	18	39

a Which elements will form:
(i) a basic oxide?
(ii) covalent compounds?
(iii) a chloride which is a liquid at room temperature?   (3)

b Which element has:
(i) 12 neutrons in it nucleus?
(ii) an ion with electronic structure 2, 8, 8?
(iii) an isotope $^{34}_{16}X$?   (3)

16 The graph below follows the amount of CO_2 evolved when 1g of marble chips dissolves in an excess amount of 2 M nitric acid.

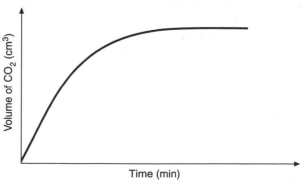

a Sketch the graph that would result if the marble were powdered. (2)

b Sketch the graph that would result if excess 1 M nitric acid were reacted with 1g of marble chips. (2)

17 Four elements A, D, E, and G have the following atomic numbers:
A = 10; D = 11; E = 17; G = 19.

a Which one of A, E, and G will have similar properties to D? (1)

b Which of these four elements will be in the same group of the periodic table as argon (electronic structure 2, 8, 8)? (1)

18 The diagrams show the arrangement of the hydrocarbon chains in three synthetic polymer materials.

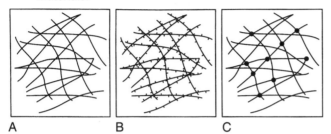

A   B   C

a Which polymer is a thermoset? (1)
b Which polymer softens at the lowest temperature? (1)
c Explain why Polymer A has the lowest density. (2)

19 Label each of the following rocks either sedimentary, igneous or metamorphic. (3)
a hard with large crystals
b no crystals, no fossils
c soft with fossils

20 This table gives the properties of some materials.

Properties	Use
flammable volatile liquid	
flexible ductile conductor	
rigid mouldable insulator	
non-flammable and inert gas	
cheap dense solid with high compressive strength	
light solid with high tensile strength	

Complete the 'Use' column in the table by choosing letters from the following: (6)
A the body of an electric plug
B the wings of an aircraft
C the fuel for a car
D the supports of a motorway bridge
E the filling of an electric light bulb
F the wire inside an electric cable

21 Lucien is trying to make pure sugar crystals from sugar-beet. Help him by listing these practical steps in the correct order. (3)

A	crystallize	**B**	chop/mince
C	evaporate	**D**	boil in water
E	filter	**F**	redissolve/recrystallize

22 *Magma* cools to make *igneous rocks* which are then weathered to form *sedimentary rocks*. These rocks can also change into metamorphic rocks which can then weather or be incorporated again into molten magma. This series of changes makes up the rock cycle. Draw a labelled diagram of the rock cycle. Include the words *erosion/transport*, *deposition* and *heat/pressure*. (4)

23 This is a diagram of a fractional distillation column used in an oil refinery.

a label the coolest part inside the fractionating column with a star (*). (1)
b What happens to vapour as it rises through a bubble cap (e.g. B)? (2)
c What happens to a liquid that passes down through the tubes labelled A? (1)
d From which of the pipes C–I will flow the hydrocarbon C_3H_6? (1)
e The hydrocarbon $C_{10}H_{22}$ passes into a catalytic cracker. One product of cracking is propene C_3H_6. Give the formula of the other product. (2)
f Propene is used to make a polymer called a polypropene. Give the structures of propene and a section of polypropene. Explain how propene polymerizes to make polypropene molecules. (4)

24 Methane, carbon dioxide, and oxides of nitrogen are greenhouse gases. Give the major source of each gas. Describe how scientists believe greenhouse gases contribute to global warming. (4)

25 Mary pours 50cm³ of water into a measuring cylinder and then adds a piece of rock. The water level goes up to 85cm³ and then slowly falls to 83cm³.

   a   Why does the water level slowly fall? (1)

   b   What will Mary see as the water level falls? (1)

   c   Which sort of rock is it *least* likely to be; sedimentary, igneous or metamorphic? (1)

26 Sandy's teacher asks her to make pure salt from a lump of mineral rock salt. Label these steps (1–2–3–4–5–6–7) in the right order so that Sandy will end up with pure dry crystals of salt. (3)

Order	Step
	Filter
	Press between dry filter papers
	Stir with hot water
	Wash quickly with cold water
	Evaporate
	Crush
	Cool and crystallise

Large amounts of ammonia are needed to make fertilizers. Ammonia is made by the Haber process that uses an iron catalyst to combine hydrogen and nitrogen and nitrogen gases at 450°C and 150 atmospheres pressure.

$$3H_2(g) + N_2(g) \rightleftharpoons 2NH_3(g)$$

The yield of ammonia increases as temperature decreases and as pressure increases.

   a   What is the relationship between temperature and the rate of the reaction? (1)

   b   Highest yields are obtained at temperatures below 350°C. Why is the Haber process usually run at 450°C? (2)

   c   Why does increasing the pressure increase the rate of the reaction? (1)

   d   Suppose a Haber process reactor vessel bursts open. What would be the volume of 1m³ of reactants (at 450°C/150 atmos.) under external conditions (27°C and 1 atmos.)? (3)

Answers

(Short answers only)

2 **a** purple
   b red
   c orange
   d pale red

3 **a** $CaCO_{3(s)} + 2HNO_{3\ (aq)} \rightarrow CO_{2(g)} +$
     $Ca(NO_3)_{2\ (aq)} + H_2O_{(l)}$
   b RMM of $CaCO_3$ = 100g $\Rightarrow$ 10g = 0.1 mol $CaCO_3$
     from the equation this gives 0.1 mol CO_2
     RMM of CO_2 = 44g therefore 4.4g CO_2 evolved

4 **a** paraffin wax
   b heat energy
   c carbon dioxide and steam
   d oxygen

5 **a** OC, C, M, IC
   b It is under enormous pressure which raises its melting point.

6

Salt	Metal/metal compound	Acid
zinc sulphate	*zinc; zinc oxide/ hydroxide/carbonate*	sulphuric acid
lead nitrate	lead carbonate	nitric acid
sodium chloride	*sodium carbonate/ hydroxide/oxide*	hydrochloric acid
copper sulphate	*copper oxide/ carbonate/hydroxide*	sulphuric acid

9 **a** atoms, ions, molecules
   b The ionic bonds that exist between the sodium and chloride ions are much stronger than the bonds which hold the water molecules together. Therefore less energy is required to split the water molecules into liquid form than is required to melt the sodium chloride.
   c In a liquid the ions can move, carrying a charge through the solution, while in a solid state the sodium and chloride ions are held fixed in the lattice so no charge is carried across.

11 **a** B, A, D, C
   b Yes, because A is more reactive than B a reaction will take place. The more reactive metal, A, will go into solution displacing either hydrogen from the solution or metal B if it is below hydrogen in the reactivity list.

12

Electrolysis system	At the anode (+)	At the cathode (-)
Copper sulphate between copper electrodes	anode dissolves	copper deposits
Dilute sulphuric acid between carbon electrodes	oxygen collects	hydrogen collects

13 **a** oxygen and water
   b The water in bogs is very still and there is little mixing between the surface water which contains oxygen from the air, and the deep water which has little oxygen dissolved in it. The swords buried deep in the bog are in contact with water, but not oxygen. Without oxygen rusting will not take place.
   c Both rusting and combustion require oxygen.

14 1, 2, 4, 3

15 **a** **(i)** A or B
     (ii) C
     (iii) C
   b **(i)** A
     (ii) B or C
     (iii) C

17 **a** G
   b A

18 **a** C
   b A

19 **a** igneous
   b metamorphic
   c sedimentary

20 C, F, A, E, D, B

21 B, D, E, C, A, F

23 **b** As the vapour passes through the bubble cap, it comes into contact with liquid in the collecting tray. This cools the vapour to the temperature of the liquid, and fractions which boil at or above this temperature will condense.
   c The liquid will fall into the hotter liquid in the collecting tray below where it will vapourise and pass back up through the bubble cap.
   d C
   e C_7H_{16}
   f

propene   poly-propene

During polymerisation one of the bonds making the double bond in propene molecules breaks. The electrons from the broken bonds form two new single bonds with neighbouring propene molecules. Gradually long chains form.

25 **a** The water level falls as the rock is porous and water seeps into the holes producing a fall in volume.
   b Air bubbles will rise as the water falls.
   c Metamorphic.

26 3, 7, 2, 6, 4, 1, 5

27 a Rate is proportional to temperature.

   b The reaction slows down as the temperature falls, so even though there is a high yield this is obtained too slowly to be viable.

   c The increase in pressure pushes the reacting molecules closer together. This means they have a greater chance of colliding and therefore reacting.

   d $62.2 m^3$

INDEX

Entries in **bold** type indicate main topic entries.

Periodic table

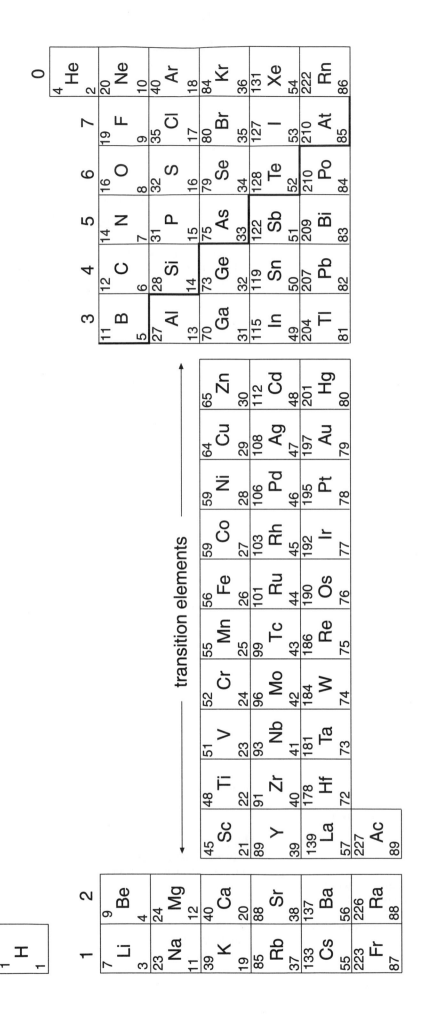